HYPERACTIVITY
What's the alternative
?

Maggie Jones is the author of fifteen books, both non-fiction and fiction. She specializes in health issues, writing regularly for national magazines and newspapers, and has a particular interest in children's health.

HYPERACTIVITY
What's the alternative ?

Help your child
overcome
Attention Deficit
Hyperactivity Disorder

Maggie Jones

ELEMENT
Shaftesbury, Dorset • Boston, Massachusetts • Melbourne, Victoria

©Element Books Limited 2000
Text ©Maggie Jones 2000

First published in the UK in 2000 by
Element Books Limited
Shaftesbury, Dorset SP7 8BP

Published in the US in 2000 by
Element Books, Inc
160 North Washington Street
Boston, MA 02114

Published in Australia in 2000 by
Element Books and distributed by
Penguin Australia Limited
487 Maroondah Highway, Ringwood,
Victoria 3134

Cover design by:
THE BRIDGEWATER BOOK COMPANY
Design and Typeset by:
THE BRIDGEWATER BOOK COMPANY
Cover photograph by: Ian Parsons
Printed and bound in Great Britain by Creative Print and Design (Wales), Ebbw Vale

British Library Cataloguing in Publication data available

Library of Congress Cataloging in Publication data available

ISBN 1 86204 580 1

Contents

Introduction

'**M**Y CHILD is hyperactive' is a common enough statement which can be heard in every playgroup, mother and toddler group and school playground throughout the country. Although it is commonly used, 'hyperactivity' is a much abused term. Surveys show that as many as 30 per cent of parents describe their child as 'hyperactive' at least some of the time. About one in ten parents would say that their child had a serious hyperactivity problem. North American researchers have estimated that between 5–8 per cent of children have this problem, while experts in the UK believe the number of children with true hyperactivity to be as few as one in 100 or even one in 200.

While there has been much controversy over the causes and the exact definition of this syndrome, and the numbers of children affected, hyperactivity is now recognized by the medical profession, and is now known as Attention Deficit

Disorder (ADD) – or Attention Deficit Hyperactivity Disorder (ADHD). It is sometimes still referred to as the 'hyperkinetic syndrome' though this term is now falling out of use.

Some doctors believe hyperactivity is, in fact, simply one end of the normal spectrum of behaviour; everyone knows that some children are much more active than others and have a more impulsive or curious temperament, and some children also clearly need less sleep than others. These tendencies are often inherited, so there is some truth in the suspicion that some children are simply 'born hyperactive', and parents who were hyperactive themselves are much more likely to have hyperactive children. Studies of twins also show a genetic factor, with 50 per cent of identical twins both being hyperactive. Recent research has pointed to brain differences in hyperactive children (see chapter one).

In some rare cases, hyperactivity may be the result of minor brain damage caused during pregnancy or birth. It may also be caused by chemicals and other harmful substances in the environment. Hyperactivity has recently been linked to lead poisoning, which is far more common than previously thought, and to artificial chemicals in the diet such as colourings, flavourings and preservatives. Hyperactivity can also be linked to drugs, such as steroids, which are commonly used in the treatment of eczema, asthma and other allergies common in childhood. Hyperactive behaviour in children has also been linked to caffeine – found in soft drinks, chocolate and confectionery – and to food allergies and food intolerance.

Of all the controversies that have surrounded the causes and treatment of hyperactivity, none has been more contentious than the question of diet. Many books and articles have been published claiming that the major cause of hyperactivity is intolerance to certain foods, and that therefore the main treatment is to identify and eliminate these from the diet. Many support groups for parents of hyperactive children recommend certain diets and parents claim varying degrees of success. Doctors are very much divided on the issue of diet, with some supporting the theory and others completely dismissing it. A number of diets exist for treating hyperactive children, which will be looked at in chapter two.

Boys are far more likely to be diagnosed as being hyperactive – about four or five times more likely – than are girls. While there may be a genetic basis for this, it may also partly be because boys generally seem to be more physically loud and active than girls, and so if this tendency is exaggerated it is likely to be more problematic. Boys may actually be encouraged to be more physically active: quiet, shy boys are often seen as 'wimps'. Boys are expected to be more aggressive, outgoing and active than girls, so it is perhaps not surprising that more boys behave 'badly'.

Hyperactivity is also to some extent in the mind of the beholder – some people expect children to be lively and boisterous and will tolerate or even approve such behaviour, while others will expect children to be quieter and more obedient. Sometimes children get labelled 'hyperactive' when their parents or other people simply have quite unreasonable expectations of how a young child should behave.

True hyperactivity, or ADHD, however, is a pattern of restless, inattentive, impulsive behaviour where your child will not sit still, cannot pay attention for more than a short time, and will not settle down to games, toys or activities as well as other children the same age. Hyperactive children will often settle poorly at nursery or school, and will tend to fall behind their peers. They may have problems with reading and learning other basic skills. ADHD often goes with other delays in development such as clumsiness (dyspraxia) and speech delay.

The hyperactive child usually does not realize that he has a problem, and will not understand other people's reaction. 'I'm always in trouble', 'Why do people always shout at me?' and, 'I can't do my lessons', are common complaints. Hyperactive children may find difficulty in making friends and getting on with other children. If these problems are not addressed, a child with ADHD may find their life chances are considerably reduced.

Hyperactivity can be linked to other conditions. Frequently, sleep disorders play a part. Lack of sleep may be caused by ADHD, but can also cause it. The child who doesn't get enough sleep will often be tired, fractious, clumsy and unable to concentrate during the day.

Many elements of modern existence may contribute to the problem of hyperactivity. Life is lived at a much faster pace than in the past. Children today have to cope with a bombardment of information, stimulus, and entertainment, from television, computer games, organized activities, after-school clubs and the media generally. While being perhaps mentally over-stimulated, modern children may lack physical exercise which would make them healthily tired. Many children do not walk to primary school any more because of danger on the roads and fear of attack by child abusers. Further, many schools, especially in inner-city areas, have little outdoor space for children to play at break-time or in the lunch hour or for organized sports. These days far less time is spent by children in walking home from school, or in playing out in the street, or playing football in the park. The modern child is frequently made to stay indoors or in a supervized activity rather than having physical freedom.

Television programmes have been broken down into shorter and shorter episodes requiring a shorter and shorter attention span. Films have faster, and ever more furious, action rushing from one climax to another in quick succession. Children cannot be immune to these trends and may expect the same fast pace to apply at school and at home, reducing their ability to spend time concentrating on slower tasks which require more long-term attention.

Another problem is the increasing stress laid in our society on developing intellectual skills and passing exams, partly because of the decline in manual work and apprenticeships which offered a practical approach to learning, The choice is now seen as being between getting formal school qualifications or having no job, and as exams become more and more competitive a generation of children are being forced into higher and higher achievement at school. The setting of targets has made teachers and parents focus on those children who are failing to reach them and, to find reasons why. As a result, children who do not find schoolwork easy are seen as more and more of a problem.

Children may also be over-stimulated and lose the ability to concentrate. While in the past children were, on the whole, made to go to bed early, to read or amuse themselves in their room, nowadays children are allowed to stay up later, watching television or videos or taking part in more social activities. This trend is increasing, partly because many more mothers work and the evening is the only time they can spend with their children. Meals, too, have become more fragmented, with children tending to snack and eat less healthy foods. Hyperactivity can be linked to low blood sugar caused by a poor diet and long gaps between meals. Many sugary snacks and refined carbohydrates cause a sudden surge of sugar in the blood which can make a child very active, leading to a rapid 'down' afterwards as the blood-sugar level drops thus leading to irritability, lack of concentration and erratic behaviour.

There is some evidence that a child's upbringing can have an affect on hyperactivity as well. Children with unstable, chaotic families, or who live in households where for many reasons there is disharmony, or perhaps where they are not given the attention necessary to learn constructive play, can become hyperactive or develop behaviour problems. It is very important, therefore, that the causes of hyperactive behaviour are looked into and a proper diagnoses made before treatment is given.

Can hyperactivity be treated?

Parents whose child is diagnosed as hyperactive have a number of choices for treatment. In severe cases, orthodox doctors may recommend medication to calm your child down and therefore reduce behavioural problems and help him concentrate at school. Curiously, the drugs that are normally used to treat hyperactivity are stimulants rather than tranquillizers. This is because these drugs are thought to stimulate parts of the brain which are actually not functioning properly in the hyperactive child. The fact that these drugs can, in some cases, be effective is evidence that there may be a specific dysfunction in the brain which causes hyperactivity.

Sometimes short-term drug treatment can help to calm your child while new patterns of behaviour are being learnt. The drugs tend to become less effective with time anyway, so long-term treatment is rarely recommended. However, many parents feel understandably anxious about the use of powerful medications on their child, especially since it is known that the drugs can have side-effects (see chapter three). The main medical alternative to drugs is behavioural therapy, which is normally carried out with the involvement of a clinical or educational psychologist. Behavioural therapy for your child and sometimes counselling for the whole family are also often recommended. This is usually aimed at helping parents create routines for their child and find ways to reward good, and discourage disruptive, behaviour.

In addition to these conventional therapies, there are a variety of alternative or complementary therapies which can have very good results with hyperactive children. Homeopathy, cranial osteopathy, aromatherapy, visualization and relaxation techniques in particular can be of great benefit. These will be looked at in detail in chapter four. Nutritional therapy can also be of great benefit, and detecting any food allergies or intolerances and altering your child's diet to remove these, can also produce dramatic results, as detailed in chapter two.

If you think your child may be hyperactive, it is very important to seek help. Many parents feel that they are held to blame for their child's difficult behaviour and may feel guilty and misunderstood. There are ways of making life easier for yourself and your child, and if teachers and pre-school staff recognize the problem there are ways of helping him in school, too. If you take action now there is every chance that you will help your child break out of a vicious circle of stigmatization and under-achievement and set him on the way to leading a happy and fulfilled life.

1

What causes hyperactivity?

Hyperactivity, or Attention Deficit Hyperactivity Disorder (ADHD) is a behavioural disorder, rather than a disease. Because of this, many people think that it is caused by poor parenting or people 'letting their children run out of control', or they label ADHD children as naughty, lazy and stupid. In fact, this is far from the truth. ADHD is a real disorder, although it has come to the attention of many doctors only fairly recently, so they may not have covered it in their training. It is found in the two international classifications of mental disorders and is generally recognized throughout the world.

However, there has been a considerable gulf between the way that the disorder used to be seen in the UK and Europe and how it was seen in the United States. In the UK, the view supported by the influential Professor Michael Rutter, who was Head of the Department of Childhood and Adolescent Psychiatry at the Institute of Psychiatry in London, was that hyperactivity was rare, and was usually associated with low IQ, epilepsy, and other disorders, and this view was reiterated in a paper co-authored by Professor Rutter as late as 1985. In clear contrast, in the USA the view was, and is, that hyperactivity is not usually associated with brain damage, but is a greater than normal level of activity and fairly common in children. As a result, ADHD was largely ignored by the British medical community and by child psychiatrists until recently, while in the USA much more research was done.

Genetic influences

It is clear that there is a genetic component to hyperactivity. For a start, hyperactivity is much more common in boys than in girls – about four to five times more common. Boys generally seem to be more vulnerable than girls to a number of developmental disorders, ranging from dyslexia to autism, so perhaps this is not surprising. Boys are, of course, usually more physically active and impulsive than girls, so these characteristics may be more easily exaggerated.

It is clear that these gender differences are present in the unborn baby's brain. It appears that a boy's brain develops more slowly than a girl's. The left and right sides of a boy's brain also show fewer connections between them. One side of the brain handles language and reasoning, the other side movement, emotions and perception of space and position. The two halves communicate with one another through a bundle of nerves called the corpus callosum. The number of these nerves is proportionally smaller in boys – and measurably smaller in children with ADHD.

Brain scanning with MRI (Magnetic Resonance Imaging) of children performing certain tasks shows that boys tend to attack certain problems using only one side of the brain, while girls use both. The scans actually show the different parts of the brain lighting up as the children work. The right side of a boy's brain is actually richer in internal connections, which may explain the tendency for boys to achieve greater success in maths, which is largely a right side of the brain activity.

Because girls have more connections between the two sides of the brain, they may find it easier to find new pathways where there is any damage to the brain. This may explain why women recover more readily from strokes and brain damage than men do. It may also help to explain why boys are more prone to disorders such as dyslexia, ADHD, autism, etc.

There may be other reasons why ADHD is more common in boys. The male hormone testosterone, which is produced by the male foetus and which surges at puberty, tends to make boys more aggressive and more physically active, and these are also both characteristics which are exaggerated in ADHD.

The first important study of ADHD in twins which showed a clear genetic influence, was conducted by British researchers in 1989. They compared twenty-nine identical and forty-five non-identical same-sex twins. They found that 51 per cent of the identical twins both had hyperactivity while only 33 per cent of the non-identical twins were both affected. They concluded that heredity was more important as a cause than family behavioural problems, which the researchers thought were more likely to be the result of having hyperactive children rather than the cause.

The Colorado Reading Project studied eighty-one identical and fifty-two non-identical same-sex twins with reading problems, and found that 81 per cent of identical and 29 per cent of non-identical twins both suffered from ADHD, again pointing to a genetic cause.

Robert Plomin, Professor of Behavioural Genetics at the Institute of Psychiatry, London, has stated that studies of ADHD have consistently shown very substantial genetic influences, with a 60 per cent heritability for the condition, which is considered to be high. One study showed that relatives of ADHD sufferers were 5.6 times more likely to have ADHD than relatives of normal children. They were also more likely to suffer from depression, generalized anxiety disorder, and twice as likely to be drug or alcohol dependent or to have an antisocial personality disorder.

Brain disorder and ADHD

In recent years, many studies have searched for the cause of ADHD. One area of research has been into the production of the substance dopamine which is produced naturally in the brain. Dopamine is a neurotransmitter, which is responsible for helping to pass on messages inside the brain. One theory is that not enough dopamine is produced in crucial areas of the brain in children with ADHD.

MRI (Magnetic Resonance Imaging) has been used to look at the structure of the brain in children with ADHD. One study, published in the USA in 1994, compared the front brains of eighteen ADHD boys with eighteen 'normal' boys.

They found that the rostrum and the rostral body, two front regions of the part of the brain, were significantly smaller in the ADHD boys. This finding indicates that the ADHD boys have a defect in this part of the brain which inhibits responses, which is what seems to be the main problem with ADHD sufferers. Another brain difference was that while in 'normal' children an area called the right caudate nucleus is normally larger than the left, in ADHD children the two nuclei were the same size. Researchers also found that the cerebral blood flow in ADHD children was reduced in the region of the caudate nuclei, and especially reduced on the right side.

It is known that dysfunction of the prefrontal cortex may result in impairment of the ability to concentrate and to direct attention purposefully. It may also cause impairment of the ability to perform certain tasks, such as the Oculomotor Delayed Response Task, which is thought to indicate normal function of this front part of the brain. The Oculomotor Delayed Response Task is a test, in which the child is asked to look at a visual stimulus and then carry out a motor response, to see how long afterwards this is delayed, to test the speed of the eye to hand response. A study comparing thirteen ADHD children with ten 'normal' ones showed that the ADHD children were less able to delay their response and would move their gaze too soon, showing that there is probably a dysfunction in prefrontal cortical activity.

Brain damage at birth or in childhood

There is no doubt that some hyperactivity is caused by brain damage at birth or in childhood. Sometimes babies are deprived of oxygen during the process of being born, and this may lead to behavioural disorders or hyperactivity. However, most babies who have a difficult birth are not affected in this way, and this is not the cause of hyperactivity in most children.

Damage can be caused to the developing brain during pregnancy if mothers drink excessive alcohol, take drugs, or smoke heavily. The foetal alcohol syndrome often includes hyperactivity.

Brain damage from an accident causing a blow to the head may cause hyperactivity as well as other symptoms, but this is an unusual cause and most parents will be aware of the cause if their child's behaviour changes after a head injury.

Difficult temperament and slow developers

Babies are all born different and vary enormously in their needs for sleep and in their activity levels. There are the 'good' babies who sleep all day, waking only to feed, and there are others who are wakeful but on the whole content, who are happy to lie on the floor, gurgle, and wave their arms and legs about. Others are happy as long as they are held and carried around, and others are difficult, fretful, sometimes hard to feed, and cry a lot. They may be easily woken from sleep, jerk their limbs around and be difficult to pacify.

Many such infants start off difficult, but settle down and by the time they are toddlers are playing and sleeping just like other children. In some, however, the difficulties continue. The toddler may be extremely active, into everything, easily bored, and very demanding. At the extreme of this normal behaviour there is hyperactivity. The line between the normally active and the abnormally hyperactive child may be a narrow one.

Children's moods are also important. The child who is extremely physically active but who smiles, laughs, and is happy is much easier to deal with than an equally active child who cries, is cranky and unhappy. Different children suit different parents, too. The active baby who has active parents who love rough play, being out of doors, and are always on the go, may fit in well, while the same child whose parents are quiet and love to be indoors relaxing or reading books may end up totally frustrated, while driving her parents up the wall.

Some children develop more slowly than others. This may not be permanent; often a slow developer will catch up and soon be on the same level as other children of the same age. There is some evidence that some hyperactivity may just be a form of slow development. These may be the children who tend to 'grow out of it' and settle down before they reach their teens.

Diet

There have been various theories about the role of nutrition in hyperactivity, including the fact that children may have sensitivities and allergies to particular foods. Diagnosis of food allergies and intolerances, and diets to help with these, will be looked at in chapter two. However, there are also theories that hyperactivity may be caused by a metabolic disorder.

Some research has pointed to the fact that ADHD children may be short of minerals and vitamins in their diet and that this may be the cause of their condition. Zinc, magnesium, Vitamin C and Vitamins B3, B6 and B12 (folic acid) have all been implicated, and are linked to the metabolism of essential fatty acids. An Israeli team who published their research on vitamin and mineral deficiencies in children with ADHD in 1996, found that zinc levels were significantly lower in the group of ADHD children than in the control group. Similar findings have also been published elsewhere. The best way to make sure that your child gets all these vitamins and minerals is for them to eat a healthy, balanced diet. However, children whose diet is restricted due to food allergies may find themselves short of certain vitamins and minerals, as may 'faddy' eaters. In these cases your child may benefit from dietary supplements. You may need to talk to your doctor, health visitor or a dietician about the recommended dose.

OTHER LINKS

Research has also pointed to other possible dietary factors as a cause of hyperactivity. One of these is the fact that a diet which is too rich in certain proteins may result in the build-up of a substance called P-cresol which may be toxic to the nervous system (as suggested by experiments with laboratory rats). The CSIRO Division of Food Research in Australia carried out this research, and concluded that children consuming large quantities of tyrosine may build up excessive quantities of its breakdown product, P-cresol, in their bodies. This may be due to an enzyme deficiency in hyperactive children. Researchers at Queen Charlotte's Hospital in London, England, backed this up when they discovered that certain food additives impaired the usual methods by which the body gets rid of P-cresol. This may explain the role of additives in hyperactivity and may also explain why some hyperactive children will improve when put on a milk-free diet (milk contains a lot of tyrosine).

ESSENTIAL FATTY ACIDS (EFAS)

One new line of research, which is quite promising, is the link between ADHD and a lack of essential fatty acids (EFAs) which have to be taken in the diet because the body cannot metabolize them, and they are necessary for a wide range of biochemical reactions needed for the healthy working of the body. Children with ADHD may be lacking in EFAs either because they do not get enough in their diet, because they cannot absorb dietary EFAs normally from their gut, because they have a higher than usual requirement, or because their body cannot metabolize EFAs normally. Many parents of hyperactive children say that their children show an excessive thirst, and this is a symptom of an EFA deficiency in the body.

This deficiency may go back to before the birth. Low intakes of EFAs in pregnant women have been linked to an increased risk of ADHD, dyslexia, autism, and schizophrenia. A lack of essential EFAs during pregnancy is common, and recently the World Health Organisation said that the recent trend of eating a low-fat diet, with skimmed milk and low-fat yoghurts means that some pregnant women are not getting all the fats they need. A healthy adult woman needs 6–10 grams of EFAs every day, while in pregnancy this almost doubles to about 14 grams.

Even after the birth, your baby needs a good intake of EFAs, especially one fatty acid called docosahexanoic acid (DHA), which is important for the development of the brain and eyes, as your baby is unable to make any of this acid for herself until she is at least four months. Breast milk is rich in DHA so this is the preferred way to feed. Research has shown that babies fed breast milk or formula enriched with DHA have better visual acuity than those fed on formula without DHA added. It has also been found that lack of omega-3 EFA is linked to behavioural and learning problems, while lack of omega-6 is associated with lower immunity.

EFAs are found naturally in vegetables, salads, nuts and seeds, and in seafood and a diet high in these foodstuffs should overcome any deficiency. The two main EFA supplements are evening primrose oil, which contains gamma-linoleic acids, and fish oil which contains docosahexaenoic and eicosapentanoeic acids.

EVENING PRIMROSE OIL

Evening primrose oil has been found by many to be helpful in treating hyperactivity. It is a natural oil derived from the seeds of specific varieties of the evening primrose plant. The oil is rich in the essential fatty acid gamma-linoleic acid (GLA). GLA is normally made by the body from the fatty acid linoleic acid which occurs widely in a normal diet.

Researchers at Purdue University in the USA have carried out tests which demonstrated that some boys with ADHD may have difficulty metabolizing essential fatty acids. They may lack the enzyme, delta-6-desaturase, necessary to convert cislinoleic acid from foodstuffs into GLA. GLA is involved in the production of prostaglandins which are involved in the immune system and in behaviour. Adding GLA to the diet may therefore help make up for this deficit and improve the hyperactive child's behaviour.

CAFFEINE

It is well known that caffeine is a stimulant and can cause adults to become tense, irritable and to have problems sleeping after taking large quantities. However, it is not commonly known that many soft drinks contain surprising amounts of caffeine, and that children react more to caffeine than adults, especially when they are young.

Caffeine cannot in fact be metabolized at all by small babies. Mothers who breastfeed their babies and drink large quantities of coffee will probably notice that their baby becomes very cranky and will not sleep, as the mother's breast milk will contain about 50 per cent of the level of caffeine in their bloodstream. Since your baby cannot eliminate the caffeine, it will stay in her system causing irritability and sleeplessness long after you stop noticing any effect.

Scientific studies have shown that caffeine affects sleep and causes restless movements, and is also known to enhance an athlete's performance. In excess it can cause shakiness and trembling and a large amount of coffee – 300 milligrams or more in an adult – can cause tension, anxiety, and sometimes headaches. Too much coffee can actually kill – the fatal dose for an adult is about 5000 milligrams, or forty strong cups of coffee. Caffeine causes dependence, too, and this is noticeable in adults who drink 350 milligrams of coffee a day – in other words four strong cups of coffee or eight cups of tea.

In children, though, because they metabolize caffeine less effectively and have a much smaller body weight, much smaller amounts of caffeine can cause adverse effects. In the 1980s a survey found that 65 per cent of soft drinks contained caffeine, and these were not just colas. The soft drinks contained 38–46 milligrams of caffeine per twelve ounces – that means one can contains as much as the average cup of coffee. Many sports drinks contain even higher levels of caffeine as these are intended to boost an athlete's energy levels. It has been said that manufacturers cynically add caffeine to soft drinks because they know it causes dependence. In sensitive children, it can certainly cause temporary hyperactivity or worsen a general ADHD problem.

Chocolate contains caffeine too. A typical 50-gram milk chocolate bar contains about 10 milligrams of caffeine. So if your child snacks on chocolate and soft drinks she can be getting a considerable dose of caffeine, which will inevitably have an effect on her behaviour, making her more active, irritable and sleepless.

Marie found that her eldest boy reacted immediately after drinking any soft drinks with caffeine in them.

'It was noticeable when he was about four or five. He would just go completely wild. Because I never gave him these drinks, it would always happen at parties or when we were out with other people, so at first I put it down to being over-excited by the social situation. But then he once persuaded me to give him a cola which someone had left behind when we were at home and the same thing happened – he became completely manic within minutes, charging around the house and attacking his brother. Of course we had to ban cola completely.'

The answer if you have a hyperactive child is simple: cut out soft drinks with caffeine, don't give him tea or coffee and cut down on chocolate. In some cases the hyperactive behaviour will immediately reduce, although if your child is really dependent he may go through a cranky withdrawal phase for the first few days and may also crave and whine for cola and chocolate.

Drug side effects

Some drugs have side effects which cause hyperactivity, for example, steroids, which are prescribed to treat allergic conditions such as eczema and asthma. If this is the case, the parent needs to discuss lowering the dose or using alternatives with their doctor, or, if this is not possible because of the risks of a major asthma attack, ways of trying to reduce the symptoms.

Joshua was a very allergic child who suffered from both eczema and asthma. His mother used steroids on his skin when the eczema was very bad, and when he had several severe asthma attacks, which resulted in hospitalization, he went onto a low dose of inhaled steroids. After this he became very hyperactive, ran round at nursery like a mad thing and needed very little sleep. Joshua's mother considered reducing the dose of steroids, but the doctor thought that as he was now stable and not having any attacks this would not be a good idea. In fact, the dose gradually became less potent as Joshua grew, although he is still a very lively and active child, he sleeps well and is doing very well at school and his hyperactivity is no longer a problem.

Lead and hyperactivity

There has been concern that invisible lead poisoning from the air we breathe, the water we drink, and in the soil may be responsible for hyperactivity in some children. Lead piping still exists in some houses and in paints which were used before 1950. Lead contained in petrol and emitted in exhaust fumes can get into dust and soil in areas near busy roads and motorways.

Severe lead poisoning caused, for example, by a child eating flakes of paint stripped from an old door, is unmistakable and can cause fits and unconsciousness, resulting in permanent brain damage, which may cause hyperactivity. Fortunately, this is rare. It used to be thought that any level below 40 milligrams of lead per 100 millilitres of blood was safe, but recent research has shown that children with levels below this, but still quite high, can have difficulties in concentrating and doing some psychological tests.

It is very important to avoid lead poisoning by not stripping paint off old doors, woodwork and furniture when young children are around. It is best to do such work when the family is away, or to use professionals who will clear up properly after them. In particular you should avoid leaving flakes of paint around which children can eat, or letting them inhale paint fumes when you use a chemical stripper or blowtorch. Even adults doing this should use a mask.

Stresses of modern life

There is some evidence that stress can cause hyperactivity. When children are stressed, they often clench their jaw, hunch their shoulders, and tighten the muscles in their neck. This can reduce the blood flow to the brain, causing physical symptoms such as headaches, giddiness, lack of concentration and hyperactivity.

A recent study in Britain showed that one in five school-age children are under stress. This can be due to family problems, caused by separation, divorce, unemployment or by bullying at school, or pressure of exams. Further, changes in school time-tabling and in lifestyle generally mean that children are spending far more time indoors, doing schoolwork, using computers and watching television rather than getting enough physical exercise. Fewer children walk to school nowadays and many schools, especially in inner cities, do not have enough space for much sporting activity and many do not have space for ball games during break and lunch hours. It has been shown that physical exercise helps relieve stress and also helps children to sleep better. It is not surprising that without the opportunity to have enough physical play, many more children are being diagnosed as hyperactive.

Difficulties with diagnosis

The problem in diagnosing ADHD is that the condition varies in severity from the child who is more active, energetic or impulsive than average at one end, to the manic 'hyperkinetic' child at the other. However, the diagnosis of ADHD is much more likely to be made in the US than in Britain. In the USA a few years ago, about one in 100 normally intelligent children in primary school were diagnosed as hyperactive, and the numbers of children with other learning difficulties as well was even greater, while in the UK, the figure was more like one in one or two thousand. This means that, according to some people, only 10 per cent of hyperactive children were being diagnosed in Britain. This figure is now changing, and a higher proportion of children are being diagnosed with ADHD. Hyperactivity is usually at its most severe in younger children, although it is estimated that 70 per cent of children with ADHD will carry it through into adolescence and 10 per cent into adulthood (i.e. beyond twenty-five years old). However, the effects of poor learning and poor social relationships will inevitably have a powerful influence on the rest of the child's life.

ADHD is diagnosed when eight out of the following symptoms are present:

* *difficulty in sustaining attention to tasks*
* *easily distracted*
* *often does not seem to listen*
* *often shifts from one uncompleted activity to another*
* *often loses things necessary for tasks*
* *often interrupts or intrudes on others*
* *has difficulty awaiting turn in groups*
* *often blurts out answers to questions*
* *often engages in physical activities without*
considering the consequences

✳ *often talks excessively*
✳ *has difficulty playing quietly*
✳ *has difficulty remaining seated*
✳ *has difficulty following instructions*

Before diagnosing ADHD, the doctor should have looked at your child's circumstances and background to make sure that there are no difficulties at home which may be causing this behaviour, for example, divorce, physical, mental or sexual abuse, and that your child has the opportunity for physical activity during the day.

However, achieving a diagnosis is only the beginning. The main medical treatment for a child with hyperactivity is medication (see chapter three). In some cases behavioural therapy is used as well as, or instead of, drugs, but doctors and psychiatrists disagree as to how effective the different parts of the treatment are. A number of studies have found no advantage in adding behavioural therapy to treatment with Ritalin, the main drug used for treating hyperactivity. However, there is a major split in the approach to the treatment of ADHD between those who favour medication, and those who think that medication is harmful and advocate other remedies such as diet, behaviour modification, and alternative therapies. All these treatments will be looked at later in this book.

Could the doctor diagnose something else?

Occasionally ADHD-like symptoms can be caused by other medical conditions. A few of these are listed below.

TOURETTE'S SYNDROME

This is a neurological disorder thought to be caused by abnormal metabolism of dopamine, a neurotransmitter in the brain. It is an inherited condition, although there are different degrees of it, so it is possible more than one gene is involved. It is much more common in boys than girls. It often begins with similar symptoms to ADHD, then the characteristic tics start to emerge, which your child has no control over. These can consist of grimacing, eye-blinking, shrugging, head-jerking, spitting, nose-rubbing, leg-tapping and strange ways of walking. Vocal tics include grunting, sniffing, coughing, barking, repeating words or sounds made by others (echolalia) and swearing (coprolalia). Tics may vary from a simple twitch to very complicated behaviour. Sometimes children or adults with Tourette's syndrome can control the tics for short periods when concentrating intensely or when they know it is important, and this is usually followed by a need to unwind with a series of violent tics.

A variety of drugs can help. Clonidine is a blood-pressure medication which influences dopamine balance and seems to help some people. Tranquillizers may also be used.

Many children with Tourette's syndrome are initially diagnosed as hyperactive.

Elaine thought there was something wrong with her son Sam when he was eight months old. He wouldn't sit still, threw things around, and apparently couldn't concentrate on anything. He didn't seem to make connections, repeatedly doing things that hurt him or provoked a negative response from his mother. He would have violent tantrums and bang his head on the concrete path repeatedly.

When he was about three, Sam started to develop obsessions. For example, he would stand and turn the lights on and off for about twenty minutes or more at a time. When he started at playgroup, carers noticed problems with his behaviour and he remained hyperactive and often difficult to control.

About this time, Sam's GP referred him to a paediatrician and psychiatrist. They said that he was hyperactive and suggested a special diet. They also suggested that poor parenting was a factor in his behaviour.

When Sam started school his problems became more serious. He was very unhappy and was bullied. Elaine had frequent complaints about his behaviour and his swearing, so she moved him to another school.

After twelve weeks in the new school, she was called in to find the pattern was repeating itself. She was asked to a meeting with the head teacher, a policeman and social worker and was told that Sam had been attacking other children in the toilets. He was copying some older boys – but they knew when to stop and Sam didn't. He was also being bullied again and was being excluded from school for his own safety. Sam was off school for eight months and Elaine was at her wit's end.

Finally, she met someone who worked for the Tourette's Syndrome Association who recognized Sam's symptoms immediately. He was referred to a neuropsychiatrist who finally made the diagnosis when Sam was six.

ASPERGER'S SYNDROME

This is a mild form of autism, sometimes known as high-functioning autism. Unlike the severely autistic child, who may be completely withdrawn and unable to communicate, the child with Asperger's is typically shy, stilted in his speech and behaviour, likes routine, and finds it difficult to empathize with other people. These children may develop obsessive interests or hobbies. Some Asperger's children are extremely intelligent but may have problems communicating with others – they have the 'absent-minded professor' syndrome. These children can be helped but often have lasting social and emotional difficulties. Some children with Asperger's are also hyperactive, and it is now believed that many children with

ADHD may also show characteristics of Asperger's syndrome. These children may be very difficult to manage and are often unhappy because they do not fit in with other children.

Stuart was a very precocious child who spoke and read very early and did extremely well at school and was also very musical. However, he was very shy and hated going to parties or playing with other children. He hated holidays and changes of routine. He was physically very active and also never slept, and sometimes used to get very upset at night because he knew he ought to be sleeping but just couldn't. As he got older, he continued to be an exceptional student but had problems in forming friendships and did not understand other people's behaviour, becoming very confused when people were upset or angry with him. At school he was very bad at sports and games, being clumsy, and also very short-sighted.

Now that Stuart's parents are aware of the problem they are getting extra help to teach him social skills. They are spending less time concentrating on his schoolwork and music practice and encouraging him to spend more time playing with other children.

DYSLEXIA

Dyslexia is a specific learning disorder which affects children's ability to read and write fluently. It is not linked to the child's intelligence and like ADHD is much more common in boys than girls. Sometimes dyslexic children can get mistaken for children with ADHD, because they have learning difficulties and may therefore be bored, restless, inattentive and frustrated at school. Once the children are diagnosed, and get extra help with reading, these problems often disappear.

Children with dyslexia are no more or less likely to suffer from ADHD than other children. Specific help can often be given in schools for children who have dyslexia. Like ADHD, the condition can vary greatly in severity and many children with above average IQ whose dyslexia is not severe will do very well in school with a little extra help. Dyslexic children are often slow to learn to read and write. They have difficulty deciphering unfamiliar words and also tend to reverse letters and numbers when writing them down. They may have difficulty following instructions because they have poor short-term memory recall. They may also have difficulty in telling left from right.

With extra help, most dyslexic children can be taught to read and write and overcome their difficulties. They may need special study skills and techniques, such as 'mind mapping', to enable them to memorize things, and help them plan and organize, which can make a huge difference to their success at school.

DYSPRAXIA

Dyspraxia is an impairment or immaturity of the organization of movement. There may also be associated problems of language, perception, or thought.

Children with dyspraxia are often clumsy. They may show difficulty in planning or organizing themselves, find writing laborious or difficult, are unable to remember or follow instructions, and have poor co-ordination. They are poor at dressing themselves, at ball games, doing jigsaws and copying from a blackboard. They may have a poor attention span and be anxious and easily distracted.

Children with ADHD may also show many of these

symptoms and sometimes it is difficult to be sure of a diagnosis, especially since a child may show elements of some or all of the above. In most cases early diagnosis and special help can make a huge difference to the child's education and emotional development.

Family problems

There are other, non-medical causes of hyperactive behaviour or lack of concentration in children. Sometimes family problems and traumas, such as parents going through a divorce, or the death of a close relative, can result in behavioural problems. It is not commonly known that sexual abuse of children can result in many symptoms shown by ADHD children. Lack of ability to concentrate, failure to learn at school, loss of self-esteem and problems in making friends are all common signs that a child may be suffering from sexual abuse.

Sexual abuse of children is now known to be much more common than was believed a decade or more ago. Most sexual abuse is carried out by members of the immediate family, with step-fathers being one of the most common abusers. Any child who has been sexually abused will need therapy to help them to overcome the trauma and enable them to develop satisfying relationships later on.

It can be difficult to know whether a child has ADHD from an underlying physical cause or whether the symptoms result from childhood trauma.

Mark lost his mother at the age of two shortly after his younger brother was born. He bonded very closely with his father, but two years later, his father remarried and he and his new wife had two more children. Mark was extremely difficult and had problems learning at school. He showed all the symptoms of ADHD, being fidgety, unable to concentrate, sometimes being aggressive, having sleep problems, and behaving in an attention-seeking way at home.

With four young children to care for, Mark's parents soon became desperate. They felt that Mark's disruptive behaviour was affecting the whole family. They took him to an educational psychologist who diagnosed ADHD. However, both parents think the events in his early childhood are a part of the problem, and feel unhappy about giving their child medication.

Fortunately for Mark's parents and others, conventional medical treatment is not the only help available. There are a huge number of alternative and complementary therapies which have helped many parents and children and eliminated or reduced many ADHD symptoms. These treatments are looked at in chapter four.

The rise in ADHD

One problem for parents with hyperactive children is the fact that the numbers of children being diagnosed with ADHD and treated with drugs has been rising with astonishing speed on both sides of the Atlantic. On recent estimates, one in eighteen children in the US have been diagnosed as hyperactive and half of these are taking medication. The production of the main drug used to treat ADHD has increased by 600 per cent since 1990, and in Britain, for example, there are now 90,000 prescriptions of the drug each year as contrasted with 2,000 six years ago. Why?

One theory now beginning to be recognized in the USA is that part of this rise in hyperactivity is a change in the expectations we have of children in our society. Characteristics which may have suited humans in hunter-gathering societies – speed, recklessness, and impulsiveness – have in the modern world become useless or even dangerous. Children can no longer play out on the streets because of traffic and other dangers, and schools have cut their playtime in order to fit in more lessons. Increasingly, the drive for better school performance both in the USA and in the UK has meant that children are spending longer at their desks, trying to reach nationally set targets from as young an age as six.

Dr Tony Pelligrini, who is in charge of an international commission examining play in schools, believes that the numbers of children in the USA being diagnosed with hyperactivity is so high there must be something else going on. His research has shown that increasing class time at the expense of play time does not improve academic results, but in fact causes ADHD symptoms. At a school in Athens, Georgia, the children's behaviour before and after play was measured. Different behaviour patterns such as children looking at their work or at the teacher on one hand, and foot-tapping, fidgeting, shuffling their feet, and staring into space on the other hand were recorded. It was clear from the results that the longer children were kept at their desks, the more fidgeting occurred.

'Every teacher knows that when it's a rainy day and the children can't play outside they become monsters in the afternoon

– they all have ADHD,' Dr Pelligrini says. The fact that children with ADHD symptoms may be punished for poor or slow work in class by being kept in at break-time to finish their work or miss out on physical education will only make their symptoms worse.

The answer for ADHD children may therefore be more physical activity, not less. The University of California's Child Development Centre is the only school in the USA specifically catering for children with ADHD. Hyperactive children crave stimulation, so they provide it through highly structured play by which children learn appropriate reactions to others. Rather than criticize, they praise good behaviour. The schooling is expensive and demanding but seems to produce good results.

It may be that the rise in ADHD is due almost entirely to changes in our society, which mean that people get less physical exercise and become more desk-, chair-, and computer-bound, and may also interact less with others. These changes may have particularly harmful effects on a substantial minority of children, who thrive on physical exercise and particular forms of stimulation.

2

Helping your child

H AVING A hyperactive child is one of the most difficult things for any parent to manage. It is hard enough being a parent at the best of times, and many people who felt competent and secure in their adult lives suddenly find that they cannot cope with the demands of a new baby. If a baby does not behave as a new baby 'should', the parents inevitably tend to blame themselves, or become very defensive because others are blaming them for the fact that their child is noisy, sleepless and fretful.

People will often assume that your child's behaviour is the result of your poor parenting. In fact, there is a complex cycle going on here. Parents who have an easy baby or young child who sleeps a lot will find it simple to create routines, to be consistent, to find quiet times to sit and play with their baby or young child, and after a good night's sleep they will feel calm and well able to cope with any challenges the day brings. It is very different for the parents of a difficult, hyperactive baby.

Often they are frayed and exhausted from lack of sleep; they find it hard to create a routine, because their child does not naturally fall into one. He does not easily sit still, play quietly or listen to anything, and parents find it hard to be consistent in dealing with their child because they are so tired and will let him get away with something for the sake of a few minutes' peace and quiet.

The situation is even more complicated if your hyperactive child is not the only one in the family. Parents are often torn apart trying to meet everyone's needs. True, parents who have a normal elder child before one with ADHD will be less likely to blame their parenting skills, but they will have less time, energy, and resources to deal with the problems. They may spend a great deal of time trying to protect their other child from their hyperactive child and may need to keep them separate from one another.

Parents may become isolated and lonely if they have a hyperactive child. They may find that other parents shun their child and do not invite them round again after the first visit with an infant whirlwind. It may be hard to find satisfactory childminders, nannies or babysitters because they can always find an easier child to look after for the same payment. Hyperactive children can be disruptive and difficult at mother and toddler groups, 'baby bounces' and playgroups, increasing the parents' isolation.

Susie had this experience with her son Ben.

'He was a difficult, colicky and crying baby. I went to a post-natal support group, and while the other babies would be happily feeding or lying gurgling on a playmat, Ben would be screaming and I would have to stand in the middle on the floor jiggling him in his sling. Then, as a toddler, he was very difficult. He would run around people's houses, emptying toy-boxes, pulling things out of cupboards or, if we were in the garden, decapitating all the flowers. He charged into other children and made them cry and threw toys at them. When I took him to the mother and toddler group in the church hall his behaviour was so awful that I had to keep taking him out, which would cause him to scream for the rest of the morning. I used to push him home screaming in the buggy with tears pouring down my cheeks.

'Of course it was very difficult for him or me to make any friends. When he started playgroup I hoped he would settle down, and I thought that the trained staff would be better at managing his behaviour than I was. In fact, they didn't know what to do with him either. They were very good at tolerating him and did their best but I could see they were exasperated. It was one of them who finally asked me if I had asked the doctor if he was hyperactive.'

It is, however, important that you do help your child to socialize and meet other children and not become isolated, as this will only increase his problems. Finding other parents with children with the same difficulties can help, as can finding physical activities that your child can enjoy and where he will not seem so different from other children. In addition, there are many practical things you can do to help your child. These involve the way you organize yourself at home, and your child's diet and lifestyle.

Diet

Many parents suspect that their child's problems are due to a sensitivity or allergy to substances in their diet. The research over this is still a matter of some controversy in the medical profession, but many parents find that an appropriate diet helps dramatically. The best-known diet for treating hyperactivity is the Feingold diet, named after an American doctor who widely promoted it as a treatment for hyperactivity in the 1970s. The Feingold diet involves eliminating all foods which contain artificial colourings, preservatives and salicylates, these are natural chemicals which occur in many fruits such as apples, bananas, grapes, plums, rhubarb and strawberries.

Feingold thought that hyperactive children might have an inherited biological disorder which meant that these substances were poisonous for them. A possible explanation was the fact that salicylates block the body's production of prostaglandins, which control many physical processes in the body. Prostaglandins are a group of unsaturated fatty fluids which are found throughout the body tissues and fluids. They function as hormones and have many different actions, including constriction and widening of arteries, stimulating pain nerve endings, and promotion or inhibition of blood clotting. They are involved in allergic reactions and some anti-pain and inflammatory drugs work by blocking the release of prostaglandins from injured tissue.

Scientific trials have been carried out to try to assess the impact of the Feingold and other diets on hyperactivity. The problem, scientifically, is that there is a large psychological component at work when drugs or diets are used – that is, if the doctor prescribing the diet thinks it will work, or if the mother giving the diet thinks it will work, it is more likely to work. So a system had to be devised in which neither the doctor nor the mother knew what diet the child was being given. The food was specially prepared beforehand and the mother, and researcher, not told what was in it.

The result of these trials was that only a very small number of children did genuinely seem to be adversely responding to substances in the diet. Often these were simple components of a normal diet – cow's milk, wheat, fruit juices and eggs. There seemed to be little evidence that the Feingold diet worked in all but a small number of cases, however, there are still many people who follow it. A better approach might be to look for individual food allergies or intolerances in your child, and then eliminate these foods. For instance, eliminating food additives alone may be enough to alleviate your child's symptoms.

THE FEINGOLD DIET

The Feingold diet involves avoiding all artificial colourings and flavourings, avoiding artificial sweeteners such as saccharin, aspartame and cyclamates and eliminating foods which contain salicylates such as:

* *dried fruit*
* *berry fruits*
* *oranges*
* *apricots*
* *pineapples*
* *olives*
* *almonds*
* *peppermints*
* *Worcestershire Sauce*

* *cucumbers*
* *gherkins*
* *tomato sauce*
* *tea*
* *endives*
* *grapes*
* *liquorice*
* *honey*

Salicylates may also be found in aspirin-containing compounds (children under five should not be given aspirin anyway because of the rare risk of them contracting Reye's disease), and medicines with artificial colours should also be avoided.

FOOD ADDITIVES

Food additives will be listed on the label as 'E' numbers. Not all E numbers are harmful; for instance, E160 is carotene, a naturally occurring colouring present in carrots.

The groups of additives which are believed to aggravate hyperactivity particularly are the salicylates, the azo dyes and the benzoate preservatives. There are twelve azo dyes, the most common of which are:

* *E102 – tartrazine (yellow)*
* *E104 – quinoline (yellow)*
* *E107 – yellow 2G*
* *E111 – sunset yellow*
* *E123 – amaranth (red)*
* *E124 – ponceau 4R (green)*

Others are E122, E128, E151, E154, E155 and E180.

There are ten benzoate preservatives with number E210 to E219. E249 is preservative potassium nitrite and E250 and E251 are sodium nitrite and sodium nitrate, also used as preservatives. E320 and E321, butylated hydroxyanisole and butylated hydroxytoluene, should also be avoided, as well as flavour enhancer monosodium glutamate, E621. E622 is monopotassium glutamate and E623 is calcium glutamate, also used to enhance flavour.

FOOD ALLERGIES AND INTOLERANCES

Specific food allergies may well be the cause of hyperactive behaviour in some children. There is a difference between allergy and food intolerance. The term 'food allergy' is normally used when your child has a dramatic or obvious reaction to eating a food which occurs soon after touching or taking it – for instance, developing a rash around the mouth or more generally, being sick, or having a more severe response such as anaphylactic shock. The term 'food intolerance' is used when the reaction to a food is less clear-cut, and may occur some hours or even days after the food is taken, so is often 'masked'. Most masked food allergies involve staple foods which your child consumes every day, such as wheat and dairy products. With a masked food allergy, your child develops a tolerance for the food and may even crave it. If the food is withdrawn and then reintroduced four to five days later, an allergic reaction can normally be noticed.

For a long time the medical establishment was fairly sceptical about food intolerances, but it is now accepted that these cause symptoms such as eczema and asthma, headaches and migraines, digestive problems, chronic fatigue, irritability and hyperactivity.

It can help, if you suspect a food allergy, to have your child allergy tested. This can be done with 'patch tests', which involve deliberately placing potential allergens onto an area of skin, usually on the back or arm. Each patch is covered with a plaster for 24–48 hours and then the skin is examined. If there is a reaction on the skin, an allergy is suspected. However, these tests are not always completely reliable. Another test for allergies is the skin-prick test. A solution is made up containing small quantities of the potential allergen, which is introduced into the skin by pricking with a sterile needle. If the child is allergic to the substance, there will be a slightly raised lump or weal fifteen minutes later. Because most children are afraid of pricks or needles, however, the patch test is usually preferred. Kinesiology can also be used as a diagnostic test for allergies. Samples of possible allergens are placed, one by one, on the body. The practitioner then exerts gentle pressure on the arm. If the subject can resist then they are not allergic, but if the muscles in the arm weaken, this is a sign of an allergic response.

Another way of testing for allergies is through an exclusion or elimination diet. This is very difficult to achieve with a young child. The classic elimination diet requires fasting for four days and in its strictest form taking only pure mineral water. Since this is not feasible with children, a child is normally given three foodstuffs which almost never provoke an allergic response: lamb, pears, and rice. Other foods are introduced one by one to see if they cause a reaction. It may take over a week of giving larger amounts of the potential allergen before a response is seen, and this needs to be repeated for different foodstuffs. It can take weeks to find out which foods are responsible for your child's hyperactivity, if any.

Another technique is the rotation diet. Here, suspect foodstuffs are given at a minimum of every four days, often five works better. You give a different meat for each day, a different fruit, a different drink, and so on. You must keep a record so that if a reaction occurs you can check what foods caused it. To make it easy to see which foods are involved, avoid complex cooked and ready-made foods which contain many ingredients.

Although trying either an elimination or a rotation diet can be difficult, the results of sticking to them can be worthwhile. It is a good idea, however, to check with a doctor or dietician before putting your child on any restricted diet, to make sure that your child will be getting enough of what he needs.

Some doctors are sceptical of the food-allergy approach. However, research in England and Australia has shown a definite link between overactive patterns of behaviour in children and their diet. This was a spin-off from a 1983 study at Great Ormond Street Children's Hospital, London, in which an impressive 93 per cent of the eighty-eight children who took part showed some improvement in their migraines after following an elimination-type diet. Associated symptoms such as tummy pains, eczema and asthma, and behavioural disorders also disappeared.

The same researchers were so impressed with the results that they selected seventy-six hyperactive children for an in-depth study and put them on the very restricted diet. This consisted of lamb, chicken, potatoes, rice, pears, apples, brassicas, water, calcium and vitamin supplements. Of these, sixty-two improved and a normal range of behaviour was achieved in twenty-one. Other symptoms such as tummy pains and headaches also improved. Of the sixty-two children who improved, twenty-eight were selected for tests to identify the foods which affected them and a total of forty-eight foods were found – artificial colourants and preservatives being the most frequent culprits, although no child was sensitive to these alone. The most commonly found foods after the artificial colourants were, in order, cow's milk, chocolate, grapes, wheat, oranges, cheese, eggs, and peanuts.

This study reinforces the view that the most common allergens in the modern diet appear to be cow's milk and other dairy produce, tomatoes and citrus fruit, yeast-containing foods, and wheat. Avoiding all these would make it very difficult for you to give your child adequate nutrition, but fortunately very few children are allergic to, or intolerant of, all of these. If your child does seem allergic to, or intolerant of, a wide range of foods, it may be necessary to take advice from a dietician in planning a balanced diet.

Although a restricted diet may help your hyperactive child, it is also very important not to become too obsessive or faddish about food with a young child. Children need a wide range of nutrients for a healthy diet and a very strict regime can be monotonous. If you are going to try an exclusion or elimination diet you really need the help of a doctor, dietician or alternative therapist to work out a menu that will provide all your child's dietary requirements.

A HEALTHY DIET

The message, therefore, is clear – junk food is out, healthy food is in. If your child is hyperactive, it can really help to buy as much fresh food and, in particular, to try organic foods which have not had pesticides and fungicides sprayed on them. It helps if the whole family adopts this healthy diet so that the hyperactive child is not seen as getting 'special' food, and everyone will benefit.

HYPOGLYCAEMIA AND HYPERACTIVITY

A constant supply of glucose is needed to provide energy for the cells which make up the body. The body keeps the glucose level stable with two substances, insulin and glucagon. Glucagon releases glucose from the liver where it is stored as glycogen, and insulin takes glucose out of the bloodstream and converts it to glycogen to be stored.

Hypoglycaemia is the result of glucose levels in the body falling below the required level. Hypoglycaemia is increasingly common, due partly to the Western habit of eating far too many starchy and sugary foods. When large quantities of glucose are introduced into the bloodstream, large quantities of insulin are released in response. Often too much insulin is released as a result of these excessive quantities of sugar and therefore too much glucose is removed fromt he blood. In response to these low blood glucose levels adrenalin is released, causing the person to become aggressive, sweaty, pale and trembly and to have great difficulty in concentrating – symptoms similar to those found in hyperactivity.

The best way to deal with this problem is to eat a diet which will release sugars into the blood slowly. This means, on the whole, a healthy diet with a mixture of protein-rich foods, fresh vegetables, wholemeal breads, and grains. It is important, though, to remember that children do need fats and carbohydrates to meet their very high energy requirements. Eating these with other, more slowly digested foods, is perfectly all right.

Foods can be measured according to their glycaemic index on a scale of 0–100. Pure glucose would score 100. The glycaemic index shows how quickly food raises the blood-sugar level. The index reveals some interesting facts: some breakfast cereals which contain sugar, white bread, potato and white rice are absorbed very quickly and raise blood-sugar levels very fast. The 'healthy' foods which your child should eat are those with a GI of 50 or less. The table below lists some common foods and their index rating:

FOOD	GLYCAEMIC INDEX
Baked potato	85
Basmati rice	76
White bread	70
Muesli bar	61
Brown rice	58
Baked beans	48
Porridge	42
Apple	36
Yoghurt (plain)	33
Lentils	29
Milk	27

EAT LITTLE AND OFTEN

ADHD sufferers on the whole seem to do better when they eat little and often, as many will be even more hyperactive and lacking in concentration when hungry. Even a normal child will become whiny, crabby and show poor concentration when they are hungry. Eating little and often helps to keep the blood-sugar level constant and also means that the child is not overloaded with one kind of food. Hyperactive children should eat small, protein-rich and starchy snacks and avoid sugary foods. Healthy snacks such as muesli bars with a low sugar, or no sugar, content, and sandwiches, are much better than confectionery and crisps. A good breakfast – a high-fibre cereal with milk, or porridge, or yoghurt and wholemeal toast – is a big help, and it can also be important to give your child a healthy snack as soon as he comes home from school. If he has after-school activities, it is important to give him a snack to have after school, especially if he will be taking part in some sporting activity which will burn up calories. Again, the snack should not be a sugary one.

School lunches are sometimes not very healthy. If your child is hyperactive, it can help to change to a packed lunch where you can control what he eats. At school, your child may be eating a diet very high in refined carbohydrates and sugars – the staple is often mashed potatoes or chips, pizza made from white flour is popular, white bread, and starchy, sweet puddings to follow. Wholemeal bread sandwiches, carrot sticks or celery, low- or no-sugar muesli bars or flapjacks, a yoghurt and fresh fruit makes a much healthier lunch, and will sustain your child for longer, too.

Give your child his evening meal early – about 5.30 p.m. or 6 p.m. – plus a bedtime snack, rather than waiting till you or your partner come home from work at 7 p.m. or later to have your main evening meal together.

KEEPING IT IN PROPORTION

It is important to resist the temptation to be over-protective of your child if he is hyperactive, and you should allow him to do what other children do as much as possible. Dietary restrictions can have important negative consequences for your child, as food in our culture is symbolic of other things: it is seen by children as a way that their parents show love for them. If you withhold treats or the foods your child likes, he will often think you are withholding love. Your child may be trying very hard to be 'good' and to improve his behaviour and may not understand why he is still being 'punished' by your withholding his favourite foods and treats which he sees other children receiving.

Similarly, if your child has food which is 'different' from other children, this can create social difficulties. If a would-be friend offers him a chocolate bar, seeking friendship, and your child refuses it, the child will feel rebuffed. He will probably not understand that this particular food has a bad effect on your child. Food restrictions can make social occasions, school meals, visiting friends and going to parties a bit of an ordeal. Your child may turn down invitations to go to a friend's house for supper because he is afraid he won't be able to eat the food, or he may be reluctant to ask a friend back and see what he eats at home.

It's not always easy to know what's going on outside the home or between children. One child's mother found that her son was swapping his home-made cakes and biscuits for shop-bought confectionery in the school playground. He would also swap sought-after football stickers for sweets. It can be very difficult to remove some foods from the diet. You can cut out the obvious sources of cow's milk such as milk, yoghurt, ice cream, cheese and butter, but it is not always realized that many margarines contain skimmed cow's milk or whey, and that many biscuits, soups and pre-packed meals contain milk products. You can get a list from a dietician about 'safe' foods but going on an entirely milk-free diet may mean buying food in Jewish supermarkets, health food shops and other specialist outlets.

It is probably best to waive the normal rules occasionally, for example, for children's parties.

'We used to send Thomas to parties with a little box of his own "safe" foods,' recalls his mother. 'We were trying to avoid colourings, tomatoes, citrus fruits and chocolate, and he was also forbidden cola and other soft drinks. When I went to collect him I discovered that he had been really miserable throughout the party, and went upstairs when it was teatime. We realized he was missing out socially, and decided it was sometimes better to let him enjoy himself and then be hyperactive for a day or two than feel different from all the other kids and feel he couldn't join in.'

Other problems commonly associated with hyperactivity

SLEEP

From the beginning, a crying or irritable baby can create havoc with his parents' lives. One night your baby will be up till 5 a.m., then sleep solidly till 10 a.m. The next night he might sleep in the evening, then wake at 1 a.m. and refuse to go back to sleep. With a newborn, there is little point in fighting this, accept the chaos and catch up on daytime sleep if you can. As your baby gets a little older, however, you can try to nudge him into being more wakeful during the day and, therefore, hopefully sleeping better at night.

Some parents find that sleep problems can be solved by taking their baby into bed with them, and this is fine if it works for you. However, some hyperactive children sleep poorly, wriggle and fidget and wake frequently at night, making sleep difficult if not impossible for everyone. If this is the case you may like to try some sleep training. Sleep training does not usually work well before the age of six to nine months as your baby is too young to learn.

The ways you can work towards better sleep patterns are:

* *Don't leave the baby or child to sleep for hours during the day. If he sleeps for an hour and a half or two hours, consider that the end of the nap and wake him up.*
* *Go out and about as much as possible during the day. Hyperactive babies and children crave stimulation. They won't be happy lying in their cot at home, but they won't mind so much lying in a pram or sitting in a buggy and watching the world go by or going from one environment into another.*
* *Make a clear break between daytime and night-time. Give your baby or child a bath at the same time each evening. Allow him to splash about and tire himself out before changing, feeding and putting him to bed. Make sure an older child has a romp or exercise before his bath and bedtime story.*
* *If your baby or child cries when you put him to bed, let him. Some children seem to need to cry at bedtime to discharge the tension they have built up during the day. If the crying persists, go back at five-, then ten-, then fifteen-minute*

intervals to reassure your baby you're there but don't get him up again and don't bring him downstairs. The same applies for a child who wails for attention.

✻ *Never bring your baby or child downstairs and play with him with all the lights on in the middle of the night. Just let him know that night-time is very boring and that even if he's awake nothing exciting is going to happen.*

✻ *Don't start sleep training until you're sure you can carry it out. If you start and then give up, you are teaching your child that if he screams for long enough he'll get what he wants.*

✻ *If sleep patterns are really bad or you try these techniques and fail, seek the help of a sleep clinic who will help you with sleep training regimes.*

When your child is older, keep to the bedtime routine. Make sure he has plenty of exercise during the day and early in the evening. It can help to buy a trampoline, skipping rope, or other energetic toy which you can use inside or out, or time him running up and down the stairs to see what the fastest time he can manage is. Then let him have a bath. After this, have a calm time with your child, playing quietly, cuddling or looking at books. If his attention span is very short, keep these activities brief. Don't let your child get out of bed and run around; keep to the agreed bedtime. If you make the bedtime realistic so that you are not expecting him to have more sleep than he needs, you should not have too much trouble.

Have a rule about him staying in his room. If he won't do this, seek help from a sleep clinic about how to enforce it. The easiest solution is simply, every time he leaves his bed and room, to pick him up and put him back again. Don't shout, don't get angry, don't smile, don't discuss it. Just pick him up and put him back, again and again, until he gets the message. He will, eventually.

Provide very clear boundaries. You will save yourself a lot of arguments and fighting if you do. Be loving but firm, and your child will respond. Hyperactive children often push and push at the boundaries actually wanting you to say 'no'. They will go on pushing until you do.

Claire tried this technique, successfully, with her son Dennis:

'The sleep clinic told me that if I stuck to the programme it would work in three days. I didn't really believe this, but with the new baby, I was completely desperate, and would have tried anything. The first night he woke and came into our room and started jumping on the bed I just picked him up and carried him back to bed. He was right back in like a shot, so again I picked him up and took him back. My husband did the same, and we went on like that half the night. I counted and we had to pick him up and put him in his bed 149 times. It took half the night, but in the end he gave up and went to sleep in his own bed.

'The second night he did it about thirteen times. If he'd gone on all night again I'm not sure that I could have stood it. We lay there wide awake and waited for him to come in but he didn't. Eventually I got up and went to check him and he was fast asleep in his own bed, looking angelic.

'The third night he didn't come in at all. He became much happier about going to bed and wasn't so tired and irritable in the day. My only regret is that we didn't try it sooner, instead of spending months in sleepless misery.'

Dr Eric Taylor, Professor of Child Psychology at the Maudsley Hospital, London, points out in his book, *Understanding Your*

Hyperactive Child, that you should not just assume that your child's sleep problems are due to his hyperactivity. In fact, many severely hyperactive children sleep quite heavily. It may be that parents assume their child's sleep problems are part of his condition and that therefore there's very little they can do about it, when in fact sleep training can work wonders.

With older children who are taking medication for hyperactivity, sleeplessness can be a problem, as it is a side effect of the drugs. If this is the case, speak to your doctor to see if the dose can be reduced. Some children with this problem may be prescribed sleeping pills and sometimes these can be given at the wrong dose or they may not suit your child. Again, consult your doctor.

TIREDNESS

Lack of sleep may be responsible for making your child's hyperactivity worse. One problem is that children seem to get much less sleep than they used to. John Pierce, Professor of Child Psychology at Nottingham University, says that little research has actually been done on the amount of sleep that children need and get, but he claims that there is plenty of anecdotal evidence that children nowadays are getting less sleep than a generation ago. He also feels that this may be a factor in hyperactivity. 'The main symptoms shown by pre-school children who are not getting enough sleep are irritability, difficult behaviour and hyperactivity during the day. We know that hyperactivity is more of a problem than it used to be and it does cross your mind to wonder whether there is a connection.'

Of course we can't go back to the days where, as child expert Winfred de Kok wrote in her best-selling book, *You and Your Child*, first published in 1955, 'Children who accept without any fuss that six o'clock is their bed-time are a great blessing.' Children under ten used to be expected to go to bed between 6 p.m. and 7.30 p.m. and might be expected to spend an hour sleeping after lunch. Nowadays, even quite young children are normally up until 8 p.m. or 9 p.m. and some children go to bed at the same time as their parents, around 10 p.m. or 11 p.m. Quite frequently they will be watching television, listening to music, arguing and shouting with their tired and frustrated parents, and winding themselves up rather than calming down and preparing for sleep.

Dilys Daws, Consultant Child Psychologist at the Tavistock Clinic in London and author of a book on sleep problems, *Through the Night*, points out that sleep is necessary to help a child process their experiences. Lack of sufficient sleep causes high stress levels. It can affect the immune system and can even affect growth in children, as the growth hormones need a period of continuous sleep in which to operate. The effect of lack of sleep is cumulative, and if a child has broken nights, naps in the day won't help although these can be useful for catching up after the occasional late night.

Whether or not hyperactivity is a factor in your child's sleeplessness, you still need to try to address a sleep problem. Your child needs sleep for his own health and so do you as a family.

BED-WETTING

It is not generally known that bed-wetting is extremely common in ADHD children. It is another chore for the already exhausted parent who has to regularly change all the sheets and bedding and it can damage your child's self-esteem.

Bed-wetting is medically known as enuresis. A child who has never been dry at night is said to be suffering from primary enuresis, while a child who has been dry but then starts wetting the bed is said to have secondary enuresis. Primary enuresis is very common in ADHD children: one piece of research found that out of 1,822 children diagnosed with ADHD about 48 per cent had been or were still wetting the bed. Secondary enuresis, on the other hand, is no more common among ADHD children than any others, and is usually caused by illness, anxiety or stress. Studies have shown that among the whole population, about 17 per cent of children still wet the bed at the age of five, 7 per cent at the age of seven, 5 per cent at the age of ten and 1–2 per cent of adolescents. So while you should not worry too much if your five-year-old wets the bed, because there is a good chance he will soon grow out of it, if your seven-year old is wetting the bed you should seek medical help. There is only a 50 per cent chance that an eight-year-old who wets the bed will have grown out of it by the age of twelve.

Primary enuresis is not your child's fault. There is a genetic predisposition, as there is with ADHD: in other words, the child inherits the tendency to wet the bed. As with ADHD, it is much more common in boys than in girls, and shows a similar pattern of inheritance, with a boy being much more likely to wet the bed if his father had similar problems. Primary enuresis occurs because your child is less able to wake up when his bladder is full and be awake enough to get to the toilet. Without help, many children would never learn to be dry at night; however, with help, the condition is almost completely curable.

The best treatment is a bed-wetting alarm system which you can buy or which can be prescribed by your doctor. The alarm helps re-train the sufferer to wake up to the sensation of a full bladder. As soon as the sheet starts to become wet, the alarm goes off, waking your child. Many studies have reported success rates of up to 90 per cent using this method.

Another technique, to be used when the child is beginning to be successful in controlling his bladder at night, is to give him a lot of fluid to drink at bedtime to reinforce the capacity to retain urine. When this technique is added to the alarm system, the success rate is even higher. It is also found that with older children, getting them to change the sheets themselves also helps learning. The alarm system will help reduce the number of wet sheets and mattresses, even if your child does not gain complete control of his bladder.

There are some so-called treatments you should never use. These include systems involving punishments, which will not work, and which will diminish your child's self-esteem, increasing the shame and anxiety he already feels. Children who wet the bed are often afraid of staying over at friend's houses, or having friends to stay, and of school trips and other activities which involve sleeping away from home. Punishing your child only adds to his misery and makes the problem worse. You should never lift a sleepy child to the toilet in the night once they are out of nappies. This helps train the child to let go of the bladder and urinate while they are not fully conscious and can make them more prone to wet the bed. You should not restrict your child's fluid intake, except possibly just before bedtime. You should certainly not restrict his total fluid intake over the day. Finally, you should never force an older child to wear nappies as this can be deeply humiliating and can even cause lasting psychological damage.

The importance of routine and boundaries

Hyperactive children often work best when they have a routine within which they can operate and, where they know where the boundaries lie. Try to build in as much opportunity for play and physical activity as possible during the day, perhaps in short bursts between other, quieter activities, so they can 'let off steam'. Hyperactive children tend to be very chaotic, and they can be so demanding that their parents tend to 'let go' and let the child get on with it because the effort of trying to create a routine can be so difficult. However, this can make things worse for everyone in the long term.

ADHD children need a more structured environment at school and in group settings as well in order to thrive. Author Steve Biddulph in his best-selling book, *Raising Boys*, points out that in any group of boys there are three things they need to know:

* *Who's in charge?*
* *What are the rules?*
* *Will the rules be fairly enforced?*

This is true for all boys, and doubly so for ADHD children.

Steve Biddulph's book also has a wonderful anecdote about a boy being diagnosed with ADHD. The father thought 'attention deficit' meant the boy wasn't getting enough attention. He made a great effort to involve his son in his activities and spent more time playing with, and talking to, him and the boy's behaviour improved dramatically. More of the right kind of attention will certainly benefit an ADHD child. The attention needs to be directed at rewarding your child's good behaviour and showing him love and affection, and helping him stick to the rules.

Creating structure at home

When parents establish and enforce a few rules and maintain a system of consistent rewards for their children when they behave well, children with ADHD can learn appropriate behaviour more quickly. You should establish what the important house rules are, and there should be immediate consequences if these are broken. Try to keep rules to a minimum and try to express them in terms of what your child should do rather than in terms of what he shouldn't. Praise your child and reward him for good behaviour.

Keep your house as organized as possible – keep your child's shoes in the same place, keep his clothes, school work, and swimming things in the same place so he knows where to find them. Try to keep the same sequence and routine to the day so he knows where he is and what to expect. Holidays sometimes cause problems because the routine changes, so be aware of this when planning a trip.

Provide a specified location in which your child will have 'time out' when his behaviour is out of control. This should not be seen as a place of punishment so much as a place where he can calm down. When your child is young, he will usually need to be taken to this place and made to stay there; when he is older, telling him to go should be sufficient. Eventually he may develop enough self-control to go there himself. You should make this a pleasant place, perhaps a heap of cushions with books to look at in the corner of a quiet room, but it should be a place where he will not be interfering with other people.

For an older child, set up a place free of distractions where he can do homework and don't let him do homework close to the television or radio. Keep other distractions to a minimum at the time you want your child to work – for instance, don't have visitors or let other people in the family engage in noisy activities at this time.

Talking to your child

ADHD children do not pay attention, and much of what you say will wash over their heads without them taking it in. When you want your child's attention, it helps to crouch down to his level. You may need to restrain him, by putting your hand on his arm or shoulder or by holding him gently. When you speak, talk clearly, and make sure he is listening. Ask him to look you in the eye. Repeat what you have said if necessary, and ask him to repeat what you have said back to you to make sure that he has taken it in.

When you give your child instructions, remember to give them in the same order as you expect them to be carried out. Be very literal about things, and use gestures as much as possible when explaining things to your child. The ADHD child may need continual prompting. This is not 'nagging'; he just can't remember in the same way as other children.

Protecting your home

A hyperactive child can cause a great deal of damage in a normal home. It is important to adapt your house as much as possible to reduce the damage and also so that you do not continually need to tell your child not to touch and not to do things. Just as when your child is a toddler you have to take all breakable things out of reach, put up a fireguard, and take certain precautions in the kitchen, you need to eliminate as many dangers from your home if your child is hyperactive.

Hyperactive children are very impulsive and may not stop to think of the consequences of doing something. Make sure any harmful chemicals and other household poisons are kept locked away. Bolt bookshelves to the wall so that they cannot tip over and put ornaments and picture frames with glass well out of reach. Make sure there are no trailing flexes for your child to pull or trip over and keep cosmetics and toiletries right out of the way. If your child likes activities such as bouncing on beds and sofas make sure this is safe. If you have an expensive sofa you don't want him to use, have some alternative such as an old mattress or a small indoor trampoline.

Aggressive children

Some hyperactive children are more aggressive than usual. Some will simply alarm other children by running around vigorously and making a lot of noise, some may accidentally hurt other children in the process, but some will be more actively aggressive. Many hyperactive children have problems sharing toys and taking turns with activities, which may come across as a form of aggression.

The best thing to do is to act at once as soon as your child starts to be aggressive. If he is fighting with other children, say 'no' calmly, and take him out of the room. Explain that it's not acceptable to hit people and that if he does it again he won't be able to watch television or have his drink and biscuit or anything else he was looking forward to. Sometimes aggression will occur because he lacks the social skills to explain what he wants to other people. So if he is snatching a toy from another child, tell him that he must ask the child. Explain that he can have it for five minutes, then the other child must have it. Try to show him from your behaviour that there is another way. Always try hard to resist the temptation to smack your child for being aggressive. A small child cannot understand why it's all right for you to hit him but not for him to hit you or others, and children notoriously copy what you do rather than what you say.

Some children are aggressive and difficult in group situations such as playgroups. Again, use the 'time out' method till he's calmed down. Show him repeatedly and consistently that aggression doesn't pay.

Other children in the family

A hyperactive child in the family can cause a great deal of distress to other children. It may seem as if the hyperactive child is taking all his parent's attention. He may disrupt the other children's games, break their toys, damage their relationships with their friends and generally create noise and chaos in the home.

Often one hyperactive child in the family can make the other children behave badly too. They see their hyperactive sibling getting away with things and don't see why they shouldn't get away with them as well. Because of this it is important to try to resist saying 'he can't help it – he's hyperactive' all the time. Try to make the same rules for everyone as far as it is possible.

Although you may see ADHD as a handicap, other children in your family may be envious of their hyperactive sibling, feeling he is 'special' because he is getting special foods, special visits to the doctor or child psychologist and given special exceptions. Children are always on the lookout for signs that one of them is receiving more love and affection than the others, which is why children will protest if they think that one of their brothers has got a fractionally larger slice of cake. It really does help if you can treat the whole family as far as possible in the same way. If the hyperactive child is on a special diet, try to cook the same foods for the whole family. If this is not possible, get a substitute food – like a dairy-free ice cream – and serve it without making a big issue out of it.

It can help to make sure you get time with your other child or children on their own and to concentrate on activities they enjoy which are not possible with their sibling around. Perhaps at weekends you and your partner, or a friend, could take it in turns to look after the hyperactive child while you spend time with the others. This will benefit both.

If your other children are older, it can be tempting to give them responsibilities for watching over their hyperactive sibling and helping you with him. Try not to do this more than you absolutely have to. You may be tempted to give them more responsibility than they can cope with at their age and then if something goes wrong they will feel terrible.

Sometimes older children will be ashamed to invite friends back home because they don't want them to see what their sibling is like, or because they feel that he will spoil their games. Perhaps you could arrange something special for your hyperactive child to do on these occasions, without removing him completely. Try not to stigmatize him too much or make too big an issue of it because this will also affect his self-esteem and his ability to socialize later on.

There is no doubt, however, that no matter how hard you try, a child with severe ADHD can have a very unfortunate effect on the other members of the family. Kim has four children: Daniel, 13; Christopher, 11, who is hyperactive; Cally-Jane, 9; and Bronny, 4.

'Christopher is especially hard on his sister, Cally-Jane. He says hurtful things to her all the time and is always hitting her for no reason. The youngest child has been very difficult and in fact she was diagnosed with ADHD. But she's started at playgroup now and is fine there, so I now think it was the situation at home. I think she was disturbed by all the shouting and screeching and appalling behaviour from Christopher.'

Daniel, the eldest, has also suffered because he has to share a room with Christopher. 'Christopher doesn't go to sleep till midnight and Daniel is at secondary school so he has to get up early in the morning. He gets very frustrated when Christopher keeps him awake.'

Christopher wasn't diagnosed till he was eight and a half, by which time Kim's last two children had been born. Kim says that she would not have had any more children if she had known about ADHD.

'I just think it isn't fair on them. He is so difficult, and I don't get time to give them enough attention. When Cally-Jane was a baby it was just feed her, change her, and put her in the pram so I could get back to Christopher. Bronny also had to do without as much attention as she needed, which is why I now think that she has the problems she does.'

Daniel and Cally-Jane have both written down their feelings about having a hyperactive brother.

DANIEL (AGE 13)

'Being a brother to Chris isn't easy to live with, but I have to. He is a mixture of everything, one side of him is silly, immature, and unkind, the other side of him is loving, sensible and, most of all, talented.

'He can't help the way he is but that doesn't make it any easier to live with. He takes Ritalin that brings out the good side of him, it has a total and major effect on him. Most of the time I hate being around him. I'm thirteen so I get fed up easily with him, I sometimes feel like the whole world is closing in on me and there's no way out.

'Chris always has to be right, even when he knows he's not, I lose my temper with him and then I end up in trouble. When he keeps on annoying me or winding me up I feel like I want to hurt him, but I know I can't. But then if Chris wasn't like this he wouldn't be Chris, would he?'

CALLY-JANE (AGE 9)

'Christopher is my older brother, he has ADHD. He is a bit nutty and winds me up a lot. He doesn't like any of my friends. He says things that really hurt me and he never goes to bed. When he doesn't get his own way he takes the house down. I like it when he is nice because he is hardly ever nice, he also hates me. I have to stay away from him, but that's hard because he follows me. When he can't get to sleep he sits on the stairs and bangs the wall and yells.'

Perhaps the most encouraging thing is that despite all the negative feelings and difficulties of being a sibling to a hyperactive child, there are also positive feelings too. Much as children may criticize their siblings within the family, they will often go to great lengths to protect them from the taunts of other children or any threat from outside. There will also be feelings of affection and companionship. It is important to try to build on these as much as possible and to try to make life as normal as possible for your other children.

Making friends

It is vital that you do everything you can to help your hyperactive child to make friends. If visits to your home are difficult, take children to energetic activities such as outings to the park or playground, to the swimming pool, baby bounce, or trampolining. At first, you may need to physically restrain your child to make him wait his turn to use the slide for example, and you can gradually increase this time so that he learns to wait.

Make sure that if your child shows any aggression you step in quickly to defuse it and take him away for just a short time to make it clear you can't tolerate this behaviour. It can be difficult if your child is invited to someone else's house before they know about his hyperactivity. It is important to explain that your child is hyperactive and warn them that he may be physically very boisterous. It often helps if you are there the first time he goes anywhere to see what the potential pitfalls are. Similarly, if he has a friend round, you may need to play with them initially to show your child how to behave and to prevent the other child becoming intimidated.

Sooner or later you will have to let your child go somewhere on his own. At some point you will have to try it out; the worst that can happen is that he won't be invited back!

Helping your child's self-esteem

One of the main problems for the hyperactive child is that they tend to develop very poor self-esteem. At home they are often criticized and shouted at, they find that a lot of children do not like them; they are told off at school and frequently get poor marks. They often cannot see that they have a problem but say that other people are always shouting at them, or getting at them, and that they are always in trouble. They may also complain that they can't do their work, that it's too difficult or that it's boring.

As they get older, if the problems persist, they may start running themselves down, saying, 'I'm rubbish at maths/English/reading'. School may be a continual problem for the ADHD child. (see chapter five).

It's important to find ways of increasing your child's self-esteem and breaking into this vicious cycle of under-achievement. When you have a hyperactive child, it's easy always to look at all the bad things about him and constantly criticize. For a child to hear all day long 'Don't do this, don't do that, stop, put that down, you're so noisy, you never listen to what I say!' is not helpful and decreases his self-esteem. He comes to believe all these things about himself and so makes less effort to change. No matter how chaotic and difficult your child is, he will do some things that are positive. It's very important to identify times when your child is being good and reward him rather than constantly criticizing and punishing him, it can be difficult, but it will work wonders..

We tend to ignore children when they are being good, and take notice of them when they misbehave, and this reaction is exaggerated with a hyperactive child. If your child ever does spend ten minutes reading a book, the tendency is to take advantage of these rare and precious moments to do something for yourself. Your child gets no feedback, feels ignored, and starts maniacally rushing around, throwing things on the floor. Suddenly you return and give him some attention – even if it's of a negative kind.

Try to praise your child and pay attention to him when he does something you want to encourage. For instance you could reward him every time he sits down to read for five minutes, or when he sits at the table and eats without jumping up and down, or when he plays co-operatively with others. Some parents do not like the idea of using bribery, but a reward is not really bribery, it's a way of giving a child positive feedback, and most hyperactive children get too little of that.

When your child misbehaves, you should also try ignoring, rather than shouting at, or punishing, him. Obviously this does not mean you should let him run completely wild or do something dangerous, but you can quietly remove him from the room, or walk out of the room yourself or, depending on his age, tell him that you do not want to talk to him for a few minutes. You can show your disapproval very clearly by doing this. It's the same theory as dealing with a child's normal tantrums. Ignore them and they go away: as soon as your child stops the bad behaviour, carry on as if nothing had happened, thus rewarding the good behaviour rather than the bad.

It is important to select the right kind of reward. You do not want it to be something expensive and giving money does look too much like straight bribery. Very young children will be happy with a small edible treat, older children will be able to 'save up' for a more substantial reward. Some children will be happy with gold stars, which you can collect and give them a reward when they have collected enough. It could be hiring a particular video your child wants to see or allowing time for an activity he enjoys. It must be something he won't get tired of as you may want to give several rewards a day. Remember that the most important thing is to praise your child and point out that he has done well.

Try to think of more positive ways to talk to your child. If, as some hyperactive children are, he is physically clumsy, don't keep telling him so. Don't give him strings of instructions like 'Go upstairs and put these on your bed and tidy your room and then do your homework' because you will overload him with information and he will have forgotten the second command before he has even finished the first one. Also beware of vague or general instructions like 'remember to be careful' because he may not realize what being careful really means.

Above all, try to find a special time every day which you can spend 'one to one' with your child. ADHD children thrive when they have your full attention, and you will find that once you make the effort you can really enjoy this time with your child and this will help the bond between you to grow.

'At one point I was so desperate with my son that I actually considered putting him into care,' recalls one mother. 'Everything I tried to do went wrong and I just didn't seem to be able to get through to him. Having a hyperactive child caused problems with my marriage and problems with the other children, and it was just too much. But we did get help, and the best advice I had was to make sure I spent some time with him one to one doing what he wanted to do. When we had these times, he would be happy and laughing, and I realized that I did love him. It made all the difference.'

Helping yourself

If you have a hyperactive child, it will inevitably cause stresses to yourself, your partner, and your family. The demands of such a child can cause problems in the family, driving a wedge between parents and causing rows with grandparents and in-laws about her upbringing. Lack of sleep makes both partners irritable and more prone to arguments. Since the mother is usually the main carer, she may be so exhausted and stressed out by the time the father comes home that she has no energy left for him. Many mothers do not return to work because they are afraid that no one else will be able to cope with their child's demands or take adequate care of them, and this can cause resentment.

If you are having problems in your relationship because of a hyperactive child in the family, do seek help early. A break-up between her parents is the last thing your child needs and she may feel guilty at having caused it. The insecurity caused by warring, unhappy parents can only make her condition worse.

As parents you need to present a united front to your child, especially if you are trying to create good routines and be more disciplined at home. There are many organizations which offer marriage and relationship counselling, or you may be able to be referred for help through your own family doctor.

It is best not to let your child's hyperactivity completely change your life. You should try to spend time together as a couple, perhaps having one regular night out a week. You should be able to find some kind of childcare that is suitable, if only for short periods. If you are a single parent you should try to get some kind of a break from your child, even if it is just to have an evening out with friends or to go to the cinema once in a while.

There are many therapies which are available and can help relieve your stress if you are caring for a hyperactive child. Yoga, relaxation and similar classes are often available locally, sometimes at reduced cost. You can also try working out at a gym or swimming to help you keep fit, or try aromatherapy massage, flotation or meditation to help relieve stress and calm you. Even one such treatment can make you feel like a new person and give you back the peace and energy you need to deal with the day-to-day demands of caring for a hyperactive child.

3

Medical Treatment

T HE USUAL medical treatment for ADHD is a combination of medication and behavioural and cognitive therapy. However, as with everything else to do with this subject, the medical establishment themselves disagree about treatment options, and treatment with drugs is riddled with controversy.

First, there are those who favour the drug approach. There is evidence from some research that giving Ritalin, the drug usually prescribed for ADHD, on its own is as effective as giving it in combination with behavioural therapy, which has led some doctors to suggest behavioural therapy has no good results in treating ADHD. Others support the behavioural approach and oppose the use of medication. To support their arguments, there are other studies which show that behavioural interventions in the classroom have just as good an effect or even exceed the effects of stimulant medications. Some experts believe that while drugs may help in the short term, something else is needed for the long term.

Sometimes the fear of being prescribed drugs inhibits parents from taking their child to a doctor and getting a diagnosis. However, it is best to find out what exactly is the matter with your child; you can then discuss her treatment. Your child will not be put on drugs without parental consent.

Where to go for help

Your first port of call will be your own family doctor. He may diagnose the problem himself, or more likely, may refer you on, usually to a paediatrician (a medical doctor specializing in child health) or a child psychiatrist (a medical doctor who has been specially trained in mental illness of both adults and children, but has specialized in treating children).

Sometimes your child will be diagnosed first in school, by an educational psychologist. These have a training both in psychology and teaching. The school may have called in an educational psychologist if your child was showing difficulties in learning and behaving appropriately.

Getting the diagnosis

Often it is a huge relief to parents to find out that their child's condition has a name and to feel there may be help in treating it.

Kim recalls that she cried with relief when her son Christopher was diagnosed by a consultant at the age of eight and a half. 'Until then I'd felt so guilty. I had been told his behavioural problems were due to poor parenting, or to do with problems between my husband and myself, or to do with the post-natal depression I had after he was born. Now I think all these problems were caused by his behaviour, not the other way round. I felt guilty too that all this time we'd treated him as if he was a naughty child. I didn't want to put him on medication but when he did take it the difference was enormous, he was a different child.'

Drug treatment

Once ADHD has been diagnosed, the treatment will usually be with drugs, unless the parents are opposed to this approach, or the ADHD is mild. The drugs used to treat ADHD are, curiously, stimulant drugs related to amphetamines or 'speed'. This seems to run against common sense, but many studies have shown their effectiveness. Treatment with drugs does seem to be the most powerful therapy available for children with severe ADHD. The drugs used are methyl-phenidate hydrochloride (Ritalin), dextroamphetamine (Dexedrine), or pemoline. Of children treated with these drugs, 95 per cent are taking Ritalin. They are thought to work by stimulating parts of the brain which are under-functioning in children with ADHD.

Amphetamine is very similar in composition to some of the neurotransmitters such as dopamine and noradrenaline which occur naturally in the brain. It is possible that hyperactive children have an abnormality in the shape of the 'receptor' molecules on the surface of nerve cells to which the transmitter, noradrenaline or dopamine, attach themselves, but more research is needed.

These drugs have been in use for a long time. An American doctor, Charles Bradley, was the first to write up the effects of giving an amphetamine called benzedrine to children with hyperactivity in the *American Journal of Psychiatry* in 1937. He found that the drug markedly improved his patients' behaviour and academic performance. After two decades of silence, more research confirmed this and the effectiveness of Ritalin (methylphenidate hydrochloride) which became commercially available in 1957. More than forty-five double-blind, placebo-controlled trials have been carried out between 1984 to 1994, making Ritalin the most well-researched psychotropic drug in the treatment of children and, possibly, in the whole of psychiatry. Each of these studies showed conclusively that Ritalin was effective over a wide range of problems including attention deficit, impulsiveness, aggression, comprehension, arithmetic, reading, spelling, persistence with problem-solving, non-compliance, hyper-activity, acquisition of information, work output, cognitive functioning, short-term memory, and on-task behaviour.

DOSAGE

The dosage given differs for each child, as there can be a wide variation in the amount given and the effectiveness of the drug in any individual. Getting the right dose with Ritalin is a matter of trial and error because large discrepancies have been found in the levels of the drug in the bloodstream in children who have taken the same oral dose. This is because some children seem to be able to metabolize and break the drug down faster than others. The speed at which it is absorbed from the intestine may also be slower in some children than others. The daily dosage needs to be worked out according to what seems to work for your child rather than being based on her age and weight.

Most doctors will start with a minimal dose – half a tablet, equivalent to 5 milligrams Ritalin or 2.5 milligrams dexamphetamine, and this dose can be increased every two or three days till the optimum result is obtained. The drug's effect kicks in after about thirty minutes and lasts for about three to four hours. It is completely cleared by the body and there is no hangover effect to carry on into the next day. Most children will have a dose at breakfast, at lunch and then perhaps smaller doses after school. Because it lasts only up to four hours it needs to be given at least four times a day.

There is some evidence that while behaviour improves with low, medium or high doses of Ritalin, academic performance is improved with low doses, but there is a decrease in performance with a higher dose. The effectiveness of the drug tends to be measured by its effect on behaviour rather than on cognitive performance so parents need to be aware of this.

RITALIN AND SCHOOL PERFORMANCE

Sometimes the ADHD child will improve considerably in school when he is on medication.

When Kim's son Christopher started taking Ritalin he went from the bottom of the class at the age of eight to the top of the class a year later.

'Before, he just couldn't sit still, couldn't concentrate, couldn't learn anything. He was threatened with exclusion, it was a nightmare. Now they accept that he's bright and has a problem, while before it was assumed that he could help his behaviour and he was treated as if he was naughty all the time.'

SIDE EFFECTS

As with any drug, Ritalin has side effects, although these will not affect all children. The younger the child, the more side effects are usually noticed, especially in preschool children. One study showed that all but three out of twenty-eight preschool children came off medication after a trial because of side effects such as irritability, clinging, decrease in sociability, poor appetite, and insomnia, while another study showed that 30 per cent discontinued treatment. Children aged five or six and up experienced fewer side effects.

One common side effect of Ritalin is that it reduces the appetite although, in some cases, children actually eat more through being enabled to sit still for longer at the table. Normally the appetite reduction decreases as your child adjusts to the medication, but occasionally this does not happen and she loses weight. Sometimes she will grow more slowly, although she will usually have a growth spurt and catch up when medication is stopped. Children taking Ritalin for a long time, where the medication cannot be stopped before bone growth has ceased, may suffer some small reduction in their final height as a result of treatment. This is usually about one inch in children who will grow to six foot or more and less than half an inch in children who will grow to less than six feet.

Delay in falling asleep can be another side effect, although often, in fact your child will sleep better. Sometimes Ritalin has a 'rebound' effect. When your child comes off the medication at the end of the day, she may become even more irritable, hyperactive and energetic than normal and this can prevent sleep. If she cannot go to sleep at night, a low dose of a drug called risperidone can be given, or a bedtime dose of a drug called clonidine. However, occasionally Ritalin can make your child too sleepy and drowsy, again, usually, when the dose is too high. Frequently, your child will remain aggressive even while taking Ritalin, in which case either risperidone or clonidine can be given as well.

Abdominal pain is also an occasional side effect and usually occurs at the beginning of treatment. Headaches, however, are very uncommon and in fact, Ritalin often helps alleviate chronic or migraine-type headaches in children with ADHD. Temporary alterations in blood pressure can occur in older children, and can be because the dosage is too high.

Other possible side-effects include nausea, a dry mouth, trembling, difficulty in passing water, rapid beating of the heart, chest pains, diarrhoea, constipation, and in higher doeses, panic, confusion, and aggression. Sometimes Ritalin does not have the calming effect on ADHD symptoms which it normally does, and your child becomes very emotional, tearful and irritable, in which case the medication should be stopped. Very rarely children have developed involuntary twitches and tics while taking stimulant drugs, in which case they should stop taking them immediately. Rare allergic reactions have also been recorded – rash, hives, fever, and arthritis. If your child develops these symptoms, stop the medication and see your doctor immediately.

Since use of these amphetamine-like drugs in adults can be addictive, there have been concerns about whether children might also become addicted. In fact, there are no medical reports of children becoming dependent on Ritalin or dexamphetamine. Some research has indicated that children using these medications are no more likely to abuse other substances than those not taking them. There have been reports from the USA of pupils at secondary schools selling Ritalin to their peers, but this story was recently debunked by the American journal *Newsweek*. However, parents of children who are taking Ritalin should be vigilant and make sure that they control the supplies and that their child cannot be passing them on to others.

DOES MY CHILD NEED MONITORING WHILE TAKING DRUGS?

Regular blood tests are not normally needed while your child is taking Ritalin or dexamphetamine. This is a good thing because most children resist having blood samples taken and find the whole process very upsetting. When your child is ill it may be helpful to take a blood sample for liver-function tests. Some doctors will take blood-pressure readings in the first months of treatment to check that your child is not developing high blood pressure. However, she will have regular appointments with your doctor to make sure all is well.

Regular weighing is necessary to make sure your child is not losing weight as a result of the appetite suppression caused by the drug. This can be discontinued if the child is eating well and putting on weight in the first few months of treatment.

Ben was a hyperactive child whose mother felt she had no option but to put him on medication. 'He was a problem from day one. He had been very restless even while in the womb, and as a new baby he could hold his head up and seemed very strong and active. After six weeks he was back in hospital because he wouldn't feed well and was not gaining weight. He just screamed every night and we became exhausted.

'The hospital ran tests to find out what was wrong, suspecting coeliac disease or other digestive problems. They though he had a severe food allergy and we had to put him on an incredibly restricted diet. He didn't really improve and finally this became so difficult that we went back to a normal diet and, in fact, he didn't get any worse.

'We did try the family consultation service to help sort out the problems but his didn't really help us. It was through this that he was offered a place at a social-services nursery. However, though it gave me a break, he was very disruptive there. He never sat still, was impossible to potty train, and was very difficult with the other children. He then went to the local playgroup but was excluded because they said he was dangerous. At four he started nursery school and they called in an educational psychologist because he was so demanding and difficult. He suggested strategies such as reward systems for improving Ben's behaviour, but the problems continued.

'When Ben started in the reception class he was very hard to manage. He caused a lot of problems – every day when I picked him up I was told that he had hit someone or thrown something. He was behind with his learning too, and couldn't read at seven. He wouldn't sit still, jumped on tables and couldn't concentrate on anything. We had four appointments with doctors who said that he was bright but came to no conclusions. In the end we paid to go privately and, after Ben had taken apart the doctor's office and he'd read through all the reports, he diagnosed ADHD.

'Although we were against Ben taking medication, we had to admit we were at the end of our tether and should give it a try. He went on Ritalin and the results were astonishing. Within six weeks he was much calmer and had learned to read. The school he was at were not providing the necessary support so we moved him to a smaller private school which had seven in a class. Academically he's doing very well although there are still some behavioural difficulties.

'The drugs do have side effects. He hasn't grown much while taking them so is very small for his age. They suggested coming off the drugs for holidays but other doctors disagreed. We give him the medication for while he's at school but let it wear off in the evening although this is quite hard for us at home. Also when he's not medicated he doesn't play so well – he's too competitive, won't share or take turns, and doesn't interact well. Also he frequently doesn't go to sleep till quarter to one.

'I know that it is partly inherited. His father was very similar, was always disorganized, flitted from job to job, relationships broke down, although he was in Mensa. We didn't have any more children because I just couldn't cope − it wouldn't be fair on the other children and another hyperactive child would finish me off.

'I don't know about the future. The specialist wants him off Ritalin by the age of eleven but I think it's important he gets a good education, so we'll wait and see. I'm not saying it's all bad. Ben has wonderful qualities, and if you had him one-to-one all day and he was stimulated all the time he'd be the perfect child. But you just can't do it twenty-four hours a day.'

LONG-TERM USE

It used to be thought that while Ritalin was helpful in the short term, long-term use was not to be recommended, but the view on this is now changing. It seems that typical treatment with Ritalin continues for several years.

In some cases it does appear that short-term medication can break into the vicious behavioural cycle, enabling your child to make progress at school, make friendships, increase his self-esteem and get into better routines and habits at home. The medication can be stopped after a while but the good effects still continue. In some cases, the drug seems to become less effective after six months or so, with the child seeming to develop a tolerance to it. In other cases, the symptoms reappear as soon as the child stops taking it, so it is swiftly started again. The research on this is not conclusive.

Some doctors argued that long-term use of Ritalin did not actually improve the long-term prospects for ADHD children. This now seems to be a rather pessimistic view. One American study showed that treatment in childhood was associated in adolescence with parents rating their children more highly, less drunken driving and less police contact for alcohol and drug abuse. Another study compared two groups of adults, one of which had been on Ritalin for at least three years during primary school while the other group, who also had ADHD, had not had medication. The adults given Ritalin as children had had less psychiatric treatment, fewer car accidents, more independence and less aggression.

There is obviously clear anecdotal evidence for the fact that medication can increase life chances. One 12-year-old boy, threatened with expulsion, was able to stay on at school and get GCSEs, which will considerably increase his chances of getting a job. Another, whose parents were so desperate that they were considering having him taken into care, were able to continue to have him at home and build a much more positive relationship. Since the prospects for children in care are fairly bleak, there is little doubt that this too would improve his prospects.

ARE ANY OTHER DRUGS GIVEN?

In severe hyperactivity, if Ritalin or dexamphetamine have not worked, other drugs can be given. Anxiety can sometimes accompany ADHD and can be made worse by stimulant drugs, in which case a drug called amitriptyline can be given. This is a tricyclic anti-depressant and anti-anxiety drug which can have a good effect in some ADHD children. It is given twice daily, usually morning and evening, and the peak effect is seen after two weeks. It often makes the child more sleepy in the first few days after starting treatment. The dose for ADHD is lower than that used to treat depression and usually starts at

5–10 milligrams daily. It is retained in the body for a week after treatment is stopped

Children with ADHD who are aggressive may be given drugs such as clonidine or the beta-blocker propranolol, which lower blood pressure and have also been used in children to prevent migraine. Very occasionally some doctors may use a major tranquillizer or anti-psychotic drug called Risperidone which very rarely has side effects at the low dose given (0.5–1 milligrams daily). However, these are major drugs and most parents will want to know all the possible side effects and consider all the options very carefully before resorting to their use.

GUILT ABOUT MEDICATING

Many parents with ADHD children feel guilt about the need to medicate their child. They worry about drug side effects and for this reason many try to give as little medication as possible. Other people also may not understand why you give drugs for a behavioural problem, while they would recognize the need to give drugs for a problems such as diabetes.

Kim says that at first they used to give Ritalin to help her son at school but then let it wear off in the evenings and at weekends.

'The problem was that this was hell for the whole family. At first he seemed to have a rebound from the Ritalin and behave even worse when the medication wore off; he would be aggressive and violent. Every so often we would take a Ritalin "holiday" at the weekend to see whether he still needed it. Last time we did this we only got to four o'clock on the Saturday and the whole family were pleading for him to take the medication.'

Many people do not believe that medication is appropriate for ADHD children. These are often people who do not have to live day in, day out with a hyperactive child. These people often say that it is society's fault that hyperactive children cannot be catered for and that children should not be drugged to fit in with a culture which does not recognize their strengths. However, it is impossible for one set of parents to make society change to adapt to their child, and if their child is unhappy, doing badly at school, and causing havoc to other members of the family, medication may be the best option, at least in the short term.

Behavioural therapy

Drugs for ADHD are usually prescribed in association with behavioural and cognitive therapy. There are many different opinions as to its effectiveness: some doctors believe that a child will improve on medication alone; others see the medication as a short-term measure to sufficiently calm the child while behavioural therapy is being used. A number of studies have convincingly proved that behavioural therapy can produce quite dramatic changes in behaviour, even when the problem has not responded to other treatments.

Behavioural therapy is based on a system of appropriate rewards and punishments such as 'time out' for bad behaviour, in which desired behaviour is praised and rewarded and undesired behaviour is ignored or repremanded. The important thing is complete consistency. It has been found that the ratio of reward to penalty in an

ADHD child is about 8:1. This means that if a child is ignored or punished eight times for a particular behaviour but gets rewarded once, the behaviour will persist. For instance, if for eight days you are strict about bedtime, but on the ninth day give in and let your child stay up late, perhaps because it's a Saturday night and you have visitors, you will continue to have bedtime problems.

Cognitive therapy

Cognitive therapy is a form of therapy which acts on someone's conscious thought processes rather than delving into the unconscious. In this it is very different from psychoanalysis or other forms of psychotherapy which deal with the unconscious mind and with deep-seated problems often going back to early childhood. Cognitive therapy starts from where the person is now, and deals with problems at a conscious level. It usually lasts only for a short time, as opposed to psychoanalysis or psychotherapy which lasts for some time. As with behavioural therapy, experts disagree as to its helpfulness in treating ADHD.

Family therapy

Many psychiatrists and others working with troubled children have come to see that many problems involve the whole family rather than just the individual child. Family therapy involves the parents, child and sometimes other siblings and can be useful where an ADHD child is only part of the problem. There are clear links between marital conflict, alcohol abuse, depression and childhood behaviour problems in families with hyperactive children. Having a hyperactive child can disrupt the whole family and the relationships between other family members, who may disagree about how to deal with it. In these circumstances the whole family may benefit from the opportunity to talk about all the issues involved with a trained therapist.

Parent training programmes

Parent training programmes have been tried out in the USA with some degree of success. Such programmes aim to give parents the skills they need to manage their hyperactive child, and have been shown to improve child-management skills, enhance parental confidence, and reduce stress in the family.

Psychotherapy

There are many different schools of psychotherapy but all are based on the relationship between the child and the therapist. Much counselling is derived from psychoanalytical theory but is usually less involved, more aimed at a specific goal and lasts for a shorter period.

It is not always possible to give hard and fast definitions to the difference between a counsellor and psychotherapist, although a psychotherapist will usually have had a more in-depth training and will expect to work with a client over a longer period. There are also psychiatrists – medical doctors who have subsequently specialized in psychiatry – and psychologists, not medically trained, but people with a degree in psychology and who may specialize in educational, clinical or academic psychology. There are also behaviourists. All counsellors, psychotherapists and analysts should have had an intensive training and have appropriate qualificiations.

Because ADHD probably has a genetic basis, psychotherapy may not be useful at an early stage. However, as the ADHD child moves into adolescence and adulthood, they may benefit from psychotherapy to deal with other problems which may have arisen in their life, partly as a result of having ADHD. There is no doubt that some forms of therapy or counselling can be very beneficial for older children and teenagers.

Psychotherapy is not normally advisable for young children. This is because a young child can't really consent to the treatment, and may not understand the full implications of what is going on, and psychotherapy is normally only helpful when the client has consented to it and wants to take part. Children who have psychotherapy forced on them may resent it bitterly and it may actually be damaging to them.

In some cases psychotherapy and counselling for the family with a hyperactive child may be of great benefit. While hyperactivity may have a physical cause, it is also true that in many families one child – or adult – gets focussed on as 'the problem' and all the family's problems are blamed on this. It's very rare that one child is responsible for all the ills in any family! Counselling and therapy can be very helpful in sorting out what's really going on.

Sometimes parents may need counselling from marriage

guidance agencies if the strain of their hyperactive child is causing problems in their relationship, or if problems in their relationship are causing stresses for the child. There are also many treatments available to help adults who are suffering from stress which may rebound on the child. These include many therapies listed in chapter four as well as yoga, flotation tanks, and visualization.

CHAPTER

4

Alternative treatments

IT IS CLEAR that in the case
of children with hyperactivity, conventional medicine can offer
only powerful drugs which may not have long-term benefits
and which can have harmful side-effects. Many parents want
to avoid the possible short- and long-term side effects of drugs
and will do anything they can to prevent their child taking
them. If behavioural and cognitive therapy have not worked,
and parents wish to avoid giving drugs, the so-called
'alternative' or 'complementary' therapies have much to offer.
Increasingly, doctors are realizing that alternative therapies
can offer help where they cannot, and will often support or
even suggest alternative treatments.

It is difficult to be sure of the benefits of many alternative
therapies because the role of the mind is so important in
dealing with illness. Most alternative therapies are 'holistic' –
that is, they involve the mind and the emotions, the patient's
personality and temperament, as well as their bodies. It has

been shown that placebos – tablets or injections which the patient believes to contain a drug but which don't – can be highly effective in relieving even severe pain, because the patient believes it will work and relaxes. Medical progress has been based on the idea of the double-blind trial in which neither the doctor nor the patient knows whether the patient is getting the active drug or a placebo. If the patient thinks he is receiving a drug he is more likely to respond, and if the doctor believes he is prescribing a cure, the patient somehow senses this and also responds better.

Human contact and sympathy and taking care of yourself are also very powerful in relieving symptoms and pain. This is particularly true with young children. Most parents will instinctively 'kiss it better' when a child has a cut or bruise, and a kiss, cuddle or a soothing rub will often genuinely make the pain better. The simple process of giving your child something to swallow or soothing his forehead can make a big difference to him being able to tolerate the pain and discomfort. The concern and interest of an alternative therapist, together with the specific remedies offered, can have a dramatic effect on your child's symptoms. Similarly, looking at a child's diet and lifestyle and helping parents to be more consistent in their approach can have enormous benefits in dealing with the hyperactive child.

Many of the treatments listed below have been used on ADHD children with beneficial effects. However, it is essential that anyone seeking alternative treatments for their hyperactive child should approach a qualified and experienced practitioner.

When you go to see a practitioner of an alternative therapy, in particular an acupuncturist or homeopath, they will spend a great deal of time talking to you and your child, listening, and looking at your child as a complete person, rather than only concentrating on his symptoms. A trained homeopath, for example, usually spends an hour and a half on the first consultation.

One mother found that going to see a homeopath was a breakthrough.

'When I went to see the homeopath we spent an hour and a half taking about his diet, his general health, our relationship, our lifestyle. She was wonderfully sympathetic and seemed to understand for the first time what I was going through. She made a lot of suggestions which really helped, especially about his diet – he was a very fussy eater and never sat still long enough to finish a meal – and his sleep problems. I came out feeling that something could be done and we wouldn't just have to suffer for ever.'

Acupuncture

The term 'acupuncture' means 'needle piercing' and is part of an ancient system of Chinese medicine. Acupuncture is based on the principle that health depends on the balance and flow of energy throughout the body. Moxibustion, the burning of herbs to stimulate the body's energy, is often used with acupuncture. Acupuncture is based on the idea that Qi (pronounced 'chee'), the vital energy of the body, flows through certain channels, or meridians, creating a network throughout the whole body and linking all its parts together. There are twelve main Qi channels, each connected to an internal organ and named after that organ. When a person is healthy the Qi flows smoothly through the channels but if for some reason the flow is blocked, or becomes very weak, illness occurs. The acupuncturist aims to correct the flow of Qi by inserting thin needles into particular points on the channels. The treatment lasts about twenty minutes and should not cause pain, only a tingling sensation. Because most children are afraid of needles, up to the age of seven, massage, tapping or pressure with a rounded probe is often used instead. Acupressure may also be a good alternative for children who are afraid of needles.

The needles used in acupuncture are extremely fine and made of stainless steel. Most acupuncturists treating children will only use the finest of needles, leaving them in place only for a few seconds.

The practitioner uses a number of clues to build up a diagnosis and decide on treatment. He needs a detailed understanding of the patient's lifestyle, medical history, personality, work and so on before making a diagnosis, and he also looks at the way the patient walks and sits, at their facial expression, at the tongue, listens to the sound of the voice and watches the breathing, uses touch – especially on areas of the body which may be painful – and takes the pulse.

Acupuncture can be used as a preventive medicine by correcting the energy before a serious illness can occur, and can also reverse illnesses by restoring the Qi. According to this system of medicine, hyperactivity, like other symptoms, is caused by a blocking of the channels so that the energy does not flow properly. Not everyone responds to acupuncture, just as not everyone can be cured by conventional medicine. But, as many will testify, it can be highly effective.

Extensive research in China has shown that acupuncture is highly effective, and in the People's Republic of China traditional and modern medicine are used equally. In Western countries, this solid research has convinced many that acupuncture does work, and it is sometimes used for anaesthesia and pain relief in Western hospitals.

Acupressure

Similar to acupuncture is acupressure, where the hands, or sometimes elbows or feet, are used instead of needles. Shiatsu or finger pressure is the Japanese form which uses short bursts of pressure along the meridians.

Alexander Technique

The Alexander Technique uses breathing and posture to correct and let go of the tensions in the body which may have gone unnoticed. Bad posture causes many common 20th-century ailments such as backache, headaches, migraine and insomnia. Bad posture can also result in creating the physical discomfort which can lead to constant fidgetiness in children. Even children become affected by the stress of modern life and develop excessive tension in their bodies and this may make them hyperactive. The Alexander Technique uses relaxation and exercises to get rid of the tensions which can damage the body and can be very useful in teaching tense and hyperactive children to relax.

Aromatherapy

Aromatherapy has been described as the art and science of using essential plant oils as treatments. It is a holistic therapy, taking people's mind, body and spirit into account. Oils from plants have been used medicinally for thousands of years, and of course extracts of plant oils are used in modern medicines. Recently aromatherapy has gained enormous popularity.

Essential oils are absorbed very rapidly through the skin with therapeutic effects. The oils are used in massage, in baths, and in skin preparations or compresses. The essences must be diluted in a carrier oil such as pure olive oil, or in beeswax or other cream bases. A certain amount of the essential oil is also inhaled, and the scent has an effect on the mind and thus on the body. Part of the oil is also absorbed directly and rapidly into the bloodstream via the lungs. The effect of the oils, together with a soothing massage, a relaxing soak in a bath, and the contact with the therapist all combine to have a very beneficial effect.

Children have a much more sensitive sense of smell than adults. They also seem to respond very quickly to the natural medicine of essential oils. Children should use much smaller quantities of oil than adults and oils should always be well diluted to avoid any risk of the child getting drops of neat oil in the eyes or mouth. Children have a delicate skin which may be irritated by concentrations which are too strong.

The best way to start with aromatherapy is to visit a skilled practitioner who will tell you the best treatment for your child and carry it out. You can, however, use aromatherapy yourself at home. You need to buy the relevant essential oils – you cannot use these neat, but they can be diluted in 10–20 millilitres (half to one tablespoonful) of full-fat milk, or goat's milk if the child is allergic to cow's milk. They can then be added to the bath water, rubbing on the skin, or added to hot water and inhaled.

Bathing with essential oils can be a wonderful experience and can relieve stress and tension. The appropriate essential oils should be added (usually 1–3 drops for a child) to warm water. As essential oils do not mix well with water, the bathwater needs to be swished vigorously to disperse them. The child should remain in the water for ten minutes before being washed in the usual manner. Another good way to disperse oils in the bath is with honey; one desertspoonful of runny honey is an excellent disperser for the oil. (Note that honey is forbidden on the Feingold diet.) Again, you need to swish well.

A massage with essential oils is very useful for relaxing your child and, for helping him to sleep. Children do not normally have any of the inhibitions about being touched which many adults have, so are very open and receptive to massage.

For babies who are colicky, sleepless and hyperactive, a massage with oil can work wonders. An aromatic baby oil can be made from 100 millilitres (5 tablespoons) almond oil to which 2 drops of camomile, rose, neroli or lavender are added.

For bad colic, add tangerine or mandarin. The safest way to massage your baby is to sit on the floor with legs outstretched, a towel on your lap and the baby on top. Lie your baby on his back and start from the ankles, massaging a small amount of oil onto the feet and up to the top of the legs. Glide up and down the legs, take each foot and massage the sole in circular movements. Then stroke the hands up the legs to the abdomen and massage clockwise with the palm of the hand. Then circle round shoulders, and glide down the arms. If he's happy, turn him over and massage the back of the legs and the spine. Don't massage the baby's hands because he could rub the oil into his eyes and make them string. Talk and sing to your baby as you massage him and restrict the massage to ten minutes or so or he will get bored.

For a toddler or older child, try a warming bath with camomile.

Inhalations are not safe for children under the age of ten, who may burn or scald themselves. You can use a vaporiser, handkerchief, or a special diffuser which you can buy from a health food shop, chemist or department store.

Biofeedback

The technique of biofeedback has been found to be of great benefit in the treatment of hyperactivity. Biofeedback uses monitors to help you measure bodily processes such as breathing rate, muscle tension, and so on. By displaying this back to you it enables you to gradually control these processes and learn bodily relaxation.

Monitors can be attached to the forehead, neck, shoulders or areas of tension, and be turned into a display or sound which will show the degree of tension. As the patient relaxes, this information is given back to them. Thermal biofeedback can give information about blood flow and help gain control of their own blood flow, helping them to calm down.

Biofeedback is obviously a difficult technique for very young children to learn. With older children and teenagers, however, it can be very helpful.

Biochemical tissue salts

Biochemics is a medical system founded in the 19th century by a German doctor called Schuessler. He claimed that inner harmony could be achieved through homeostasis – a balance between the body's fluid and acid–alkali levels. This balance is easily disturbed by discrepancies in mineral and trace element levels, and small quantities of these salts can be taken to redress the balance. The salts are safe and easy to take and do not interact with conventional drugs.

Bioresonance

Bioresonance is also known as Bicom resonance therapy after the machine used in this process. The Bicom machine is a specialized computer with sends small electric currents around your body, and tunes in to the electromagnetic frequencies emitted by every cell. Some are in harmony, others not. Samples of possible allergens can also be placed either on the patient or in the machine and the allergy meridian monitored for fluctuations. This pinpoints the allergen and the degree of sensitivity to it. The theory is that the Bicom then inverts the disharmonic waves, amplifies the harmonic ones, and reflects them back to the body, thus rebalancing it.

The test takes only a few minutes and your child need not be alarmed by all the wires, which are attached to the body with Velcro at the wrists and ankles. Bioresonance can be very useful in pinpointing allergies and intolerances and in the diagnosis and treatment of ADHD.

Chiropractic

This technique works on the principle of seeking out misalignments in the bones of the neck and then correcting them. A chiropractor diagnoses, treats and prevents mechanical disorders of the joints using his or her hands to manipulate the joints and muscles and reduce pain. Tension, stress and misalignment of the bones in the neck can reduce the blood supply to the brain and make it harder for a child to concentrate, producing the symptoms of hyperactivity and attention deficit disorder.

X-rays are sometimes used to help diagnose problems, though not always. The initial examination may take 20–45 minutes, with follow-up visits normally taking 10–20 minutes.

When a joint is out of place it can be restored by an extremely light yet rapid springing motion. The patient will often hear a click as this happens. The effect is often dramatic and there should be no after-effects.

There are different forms of chiropractic. Daniel David

Palmer founded chiropractic and his first successful treatment took place in Iowa in 1895. There is also a more recent school founded in 1972 in Britain by John McTimoney which uses a technique called 'toggle recoil' adjustment. This treatment is ideal for children.

Colour therapy

Research has increasingly shown how we react to colour, and that colour can have healing properties. Young children respond well to colour – if you present a young child who is ill with coloured paints or crayons or coloured pieces of card, they will chose the colour that's right for their healing. Indigo is the calming colour which would be of most benefit for the child who is hyperactive. Try creating a tranquil space in their room and avoid too many stimulating colours, perhaps painting the walls a calming indigo blue. Many parents have found that creating a quiet and uncluttered environment for their child greatly helps in quietening them.

Flower remedies

Flowers have been used for thousands of years for their healing properties by many different cultures, including Australian aborigines, the ancient Egyptians, the Minoans of Crete and Native Americans. In the 1930s Dr Edward Bach rediscovered healing with flowers, and in the mid 1970s, Richard Katz established the Flower Essence Society in California. Many others have been inspired to do research into the healing properties of their local flora.

The most popular flower remedies today are those developed by Dr Edward Bach, who practised at University College Hospital, London, in the early part of this century. He believed that people's emotional and psychological problems were at the root of much of their illness, and became critical of medical treatments which dealt only with their symptoms rather than with the whole person. Influenced by homeopathy, he developed thirty-eight plant remedies from wild flowers. Each of these deals with a specific emotional state or aspect of personality. Remedies which are likely to be of benefit to children with hyperactivity include impatiens – for those who are inclined to impatience and irritation with slowness. Larch may be needed for those who, as a result of ADHD, lack confidence in their ability, do not believe in themselves, are afraid of failure and so do not try. Dr Bach recognized that worry and fear reduce the body's resistance, making a person feel under par and making him more likely to succumb to illness, and that the worry, apprehension and irritability caused by disease hinder recovery of health and convalescence.

Dr Bach made his flower essences by floating freshly picked flowers in a glass bowl of pure spring water in sunlight for three hours. He believed that the flower essence or energy transferred itself to the water, which is then stabilized by mixing with an equal volume of brandy. Other flower essences are made without cutting the flowers. In Germany, for instance, Andreas Korte uses a cleaned half of a quartz geode filled with spring water which is placed in the field of the growing flower in the sun for a certain length of time to capture its energy.

Flower essences are suitable for babies and small children because they are so gentle and free from harmful side-effects. It is important to get into the habit of taking a remedy frequently, usually two or three drops in the morning and two or three drops at bedtime, to reap its full benefits. The traditional way to take flower essences is to drop them onto the tongue, or you can add them to drinks such as dilute fruit juice and water. Flower essences can also be helpful when rubbed on the skin. You can also add flower essences to your child's bath.

Herbal medicine

Herbalism is the oldest known form of medicine. It is still used by a majority of the world's population, and in fact many modern, powerful drugs are derived from plants, such as the heart drug digitalis which comes from foxgloves, atropine from nightshade, aspirin which is found in willow bark, morphine from poppies and quinine from the cinchona tree.

While conventional medicine relies on extracting and purifying one active ingredient, in herbal medicine the whole plant is used with a mixture of different ingredients. Herbal remedies can be chewed, swallowed, applied to the skin, put in bathwater, or inhaled. Modern herbalists often prescribe herbs in concentrated liquid form, but some use elixirs, cordials, teas, pills, ointments, bath additives or poultices. You can also grow and prepare your own herbs, but since some plants can be poisonous, you should always seek advice from a qualified herbalist, especially before giving them to young children. Herbal remedies from different countries may vary, especially since the herbs available will differ from region to region.

Most herbalists warn that sometimes the symptoms will get worse at first, then be followed by a marked improvement. This is normal and should not cause anxiety. A variety of herbal remedies may be used for hyperactivity. Red clover is recommended as a general nerve relaxant. Vervain can be used for stress as can gentle bitter tonics such as dandelion or centaury. Wild lettuce – *lactuca virosa* – is a valuable remedy for insomnia, restlessness and excitability, especially in children. Other remedies include chamomile, nasturtium, stock, black-eyed Susan, jacaranda, morning glory, petunia, the pongham tree, and yellow canna. All these can be made into an infusion by pouring a cup of boiled water onto 1–2 teaspoonfuls of the dried herb and infusing for 10–15 minutes. Oats, which also calm the nerves, may be taken in the form of porridge or gruel or as a fluid extract.

Chinese herbal medicine

Chinese herbal medicine is part of a sophisticated system used since ancient times. Herbs, minerals and some animal products are used to treat a wide range of diseases. The treatment is thought to restore harmony to the functions of the body, which normally means that several treatment components are given simultaneously. Unlike Western herbalists, who have a limited number of herbs at their disposal, oriental medicine draws on a range of 4,000 herbs made up in various complex formulas. A limited number of these components are available in pill, tablet, granule, powder, or liquid form, but most are prescribed as dried materials which are mixed to match the perceived needs of the individual patient. Because every patient is different, the herbal mix will vary from one patient to another. Usually the treatment is prepared by boiling the herbs and other dried materials with water for a specified period, straining off the liquid, and cooling, to make a decoction.

The practitioner of Chinese herbal medicine will be looking for a 'pattern of disharmony', which is a way of saying someone's flow of energy (ch'i, or breath) is blocked or disturbed. These patterns are recognized by a combination of symptoms, mental states, non-verbal behaviour, physiological signs, and a reading of both tongue and pulse. The concept of yin and yang, which means sun and moon, male and female, light and darkness, is involved, as often these two states are out of harmony, with one predominating over the other. Symptoms of too much yang make a person hot, restless, dry, rapid, outward-moving, with insomnia, hot limbs and body, loud voice, and shouting a lot (sound familiar?), while too much yin makes a person cold, quiet, wet, slow, inward moving, sleepy/lethargic, with cold limbs and body, and a weak voice/dislikes talking.

Children are excellent subjects for Chinese herbal medicine. Depending on their age, the practitioner will ask the parent or child, or both, questions about their symptoms and the practitioner will observe the child closely throughout the interview.

Homeopathy

Homeopathy is the best known of the alternative medicines and is growing in popularity. A distrust of relying on powerful drugs which have side effects and may harm the body and a desire to be treated as a whole person and not just a physical body with specific symptoms are two reasons why people are increasingly turning to homeopathy. In addition, it has had medical recognition and has been the subject of several clinical trials.

Homeopathy is a system of medical treatment using medicine according to the principle of 'like cures like'. It was developed as a science by a German physician, Hahnemann, who noticed that quinine, which produces the same symptoms as malaria, could also be used to cure it. The symptoms of a disease often show how the body is attempting to heal itself – catarrh is used to clear foreign organisms from the respiratory tract, vaginal discharges from the reproductive tract, and so on. Homeopathy is based on this observation that substances which cause certain symptoms can also be used to cure them. However, used in conventional doses many of these substances can be toxic and extremely harmful, so in homeopathy they are diluted to render them safe. The medicines are diluted by stages in an alcohol and water solution, and vigorously, mechanically shaken in between in a process known as 'potentization'.

The potency of a homeopathic remedy refers to the extent and number of times the original extract has been diluted during the preparation. For example, arnica 6c has been prepared by adding one drop of the original alcoholic extract to 99 drops of a solution of water and alcohol and shaken vigorously. One drop of this is added to another 99 drops, and so on, six times. The higher the degree of dilution, the greater the potency.

Most over-the-counter remedies are of sixth centesimal potency (6c) which is appropriate for a beginner to use. The higher potencies, 12c and 30c should only be prescribed by a qualified homeopath.

Critics of homeopathy hold that in some preparations the original substance will have been so diluted that not even one molecule of it can be contained in the solution, and therefore it is impossible that it could have any effect. However, homeopaths believe that during potentization the properties of the substance being diluted is somehow imprinted into the molecules of the solution carrying it. There is no conventional scientific explanation of how this could happen, but then there are other things which modern science cannot explain.

Some scientific studies have been carried out to try to prove whether homeopathy is effective or not, but since the mind is so powerful in influencing illness this is very difficult. Many people believe from experience and observation that homeopathy does work. It certainly cannot have any harmful consequences, so is certainly worth trying, even if you are sceptical.

Because homeopathy is holistic, the ill person's medical history, lifestyle, temperament and feelings will be taken into account. Because of this, there is no one remedy which will be useful for everyone: the remedy has to be matched to the person. In addition, the particular form the symptoms take will also affect what is prescribed. Because everyone is different and the homeopath is skilled at matching the individual to the remedy, you should always consult a professional homeopath if your child's symptoms are severe. Since hyperactivity is considered a deep-seated disorder by homeopaths, it is always recommended that you see a practitioner rather than trying to treat your child yourself using remedies purchased from health shops or pharmacies.

Patients using homeopathy are often warned that their symptoms may get worse before they get better, and a healing crisis is often observed. If symptoms get really severe further advice should be sought.

While every child and every case is different, and two people with the same condition will not necessarily get the same treatment, there are some common remedies which are used for hyperactivity. Stram. (stramonium, or thorn apple) is one useful remedy. Nux vomica can be used, or Hep-s. (Hepar sulphuris calcareum, of calcium sulphide). Chin. (China officianalis) is useful for disobedience and Lyc. (Lycopodium or club moss) for poor concentration.

Homeopathic remedies are usually given as soft tablets which dissolve quickly and easily under the tongue and can also be easily crushed to give to babies, although they can also be given as hard tablets, powders, granules, capsules, or in liquid suspension. It is best not to eat or drink anything but water for twenty minutes either side of taking the remedy, and to avoid strongly flavoured drinks or toothpaste which can interfere with it.

Jane and her husband Philip have two children, Alice, aged seven, and Emily, aged four. While Alice was an easy and placid child, the couple were horrifed when they found their second child was a tense, fretful, crying baby, who developed into a toddler who did not sleep and was constantly on the go.

'She had terrible temper tantrums and used to hurl things around. Alice became really upset because Emily would attack her, deliberately smash up her toys, and spoil all her games. Our nights were terrible and she would wake three or four times a night and yell until we took her into our bed, and then she would toss and turn all night, pull all the covers off and keep us all awake.

'We went to a sleep clinic and that helped with the nights a bit, and we also cut out all additives, fizzy drinks and sweets and things. Then a friend suggested a homeopath. I was very sceptical when we went, but I was stunned by how long the homeopath spent with us and how her questions showed so much insight.

'The homeopath prescribed nux vomica and we started giving it to Emily straight away. It was remarkable how quickly her behaviour improved and a lot of the jealousy and violent tantrums disappeared.'

Hypnotherapy

Hypnotherapy immediately conjures up an image of a man in a black suit waving a watch before your eyes and then making you do things you wouldn't normally do. Nothing could be further from the case. Hypnosis is, in fact, a natural state which we all experience, and is normally called dozing or daydreaming. It is not being asleep or unconscious. It is, in fact, self-induced and anyone who wants to can let it happen. It is experienced normally as a very relaxed, floating or pleasant feeling but you can also feel energized and alert. Surprisingly, the ability to hypnotize yourself can be learnt at a single session, although it takes practice to achieve a deep state of relaxation.

Hypnotherapy means using hypnosis to work directly with

the subconscious mind, channelling its resources to achieve a positive change. The subconscious mind controls our feelings and behaviour, and a negative cycle is often set up which limits us. Tension, stress, and worry all make it harder for us to heal ourselves.

Hypnotherapy has been used very successfully to deal with behavioural problems. Hypnosis can work well with children, usually over the age of seven, as the child's powerful imagination can be harnessed. The hypnotist can also try post-hypnotic suggestion, the technique which is most familiar from stage hypnotists. First the therapist gets your child into a deeply relaxed, trance-like state, and an idea or instruction can then be planted into the child's mind. This can be helpful in getting your child to calm down, go to sleep at night and avoid tantrums and impulsive behaviour.

Massage

Massage of various kinds can be of enormous benefit to people suffering from ADHD. Hyperactive children are often very tense and therefore build up tension in the muscles which can cause headaches and other problems. Massage can release these tensions and help your child achieve a more relaxed state and sleep better. Many ADHD children adore the attention they receive during the massage.

Naturopathy

The term 'naturopathy' was coined in 1895 by a New York

doctor, John Scheel, but grew out of the nature cures popular in Germany in the 19th century, which emphasized the benefits of fresh air, sunlight and exercise. Naturopathy is widely practised in many countries and is still especially popular in Germany. The theory is that a poor diet, lack of sleep and sufficient exercise, together with stress and pollution, allow waste products and toxins to build up in the body. Treatment involves dietary advice – a wholefood diet rich in organic fresh fruit and vegetables is recommended – herbal remedies, hydrotherapy massage and bodywork and changes to the lifestyle, all of which are extremely beneficial in treating hyperactivity.

Nutritional therapy

Nutritional therapy covers the use of nutritional methods to prevent or treat a wide range of illnesses and conditions. Much of the modern highly-refined diet is lacking in essential minerals, vitamins, and other nutrients. The aim of nutritional medicine is to work out what deficits there may be and add them to the diet in a way which will enable them to be absorbed and utilized by the body. It is usually best to add minerals and nutrients to the diet, as they occur naturally in foodstuffs, but often mineral and vitamin supplements are used.

Nutritional therapists will also advise you on treatments for any food allergies or intolerances. They will normally recommend a system of diagnosing and eliminating any foods which may trigger your child's hyperactive behaviour as well as a rotation or other diet to avoid any further sensitivities.

Osteopathy

Osteopathy is a system of diagnosis and treatment using the musculo-skeletal system. The principle is to use gentle manipulation to restore and maintain the proper functioning of the bones and muscles. The founder of osteopathy was Andrew Taylor Still, who was born in Virginia, USA, in 1928. There is some confusion because in the USA osteopaths are medical doctors, whereas in the UK they may not be.

Osteopathy is used for the treatment of problems of the spine, ligaments, muscles and bones. It improves lymphatic drainage and breathing and can be very effective in treating hyperactivity.

Cranial osteopathy was first explored by a pupil of Still's, William Garner Sutherland. He believed that headaches, dizziness, and lack of concentration may be the effects of problems in the skull. Many colicky babies may be suffering from the after-effects of the pressure caused to the skull during labour, and may benefit enormously from cranial osteopathy.

'My baby Joel screamed for the first two months of his life. It was terrible, and none of us were getting any sleep. I had him checked over by the doctor who said he was fine and I consulted a breastfeeding counsellor who came to see me, said the baby was feeding well and obviously gaining weight, and that the crying must have some other cause. Finally a friend suggested cranial osteopathy. The osteopath said that there was compression in Joel's spine and skull as the result of his difficult birth (he got stuck in the second stage and they used a ventouse to get him out) and that she could release the pressure and blockages which had resulted. It was amazing. I took this crying, colicky baby into the consulting room all tense and fretful and by the end of the treatment he fell peacefully asleep!

Apart from this immediate effect, after three weekly sessions he was much calmer and began to sleep much better at home as well.'

Reflexology

Reflexology is a system of foot massage which has been practised in most ancient cultures from China to North America.

In reflexology, a gentle but firm finger pressure and a special massage technique is applied to areas of the feet and lower legs which correspond to all glands, organs and parts of the body. It is thought that tensions in the body manifest themselves in the feet and hands and the consequent blocking of energy paths results in imbalance and disease. By applying gentle pressure with the hands to the relevant areas of the foot and lower leg, toxins can be removed from the body and circulation improved, restoring the free flow of energy and nutrients to the body cells.

Reflexology is not a diagnostic therapy but can indicate if certain organs or glands are under pressure. It can often detect injuries which occurred years ago, and also can detect weaknesses which have not yet developed into disease.

Treatment sessions usually take between 50–80 minutes, and the number of treatments required varies for each individual and the nature of the disorder. During treatment the patient may feel a slight discomfort on certain parts of the foot, and may feel tired and lethargic at first, followed by a renewed sense of well-being. Reflexology can create a deep sense of relaxation, which can encourage the body's own healing processes.

Reiki

This is an ancient Japanese therapy in which hands are laid on the body to promote relaxation and natural healing. It is a way of connecting with universal energy to improve health and enhance the quality of life. Reiki works on the cause of the problem, not just the outer symptoms, and treats the whole person, body, emotions, mind, and spirit. The patient simply relaxes and enjoys the warmth of the practitioner's hands over the area of pain or need. Reiki can help a large number of ailments, and because it can induce deep relaxation, is particularly effective with hyperactivity.

Shiatsu

Shiatsu is a Japanese therapy based on the same principles as acupuncture, in which pressure is applied to the energy lines, known as meridians. Although thumb and finger pressure is mainly used, the practitioner can also use elbows and even knees and feet.

The massage stimulates the circulation, and also the body's vital energy flow, in Japanese, Ki. Shiatsu strengthens the nervous system and helps release toxins and deep-seated tension. On a more subtle level, Shiatsu enables patients to relax deeply and get in touch with their body's own healing abilities. The patient normally lies on a futon, and it is advisable not to eat or drink much before a treatment. A feeling of calmness and well-being usually follows a treatment, and many people feel invigorated yet relaxed.

Visualisation and relaxation

It can be hard to teach a hyperactive child to relax, but is well worth trying. The technique of relaxation may be familiar to many mothers who have attended ante-natal classes, which often include relaxation exercises. The technique is to tense and then relax all the parts of the body in turn.

* *Lie on the floor, bed or a comfortable place, on your back.*
* *Start with the feet. Wriggle the toes and feet, let them flop. Lift the lower legs slightly and let them go. Wiggle the kneecaps, then relax. Tense, then relax the thighs.*
* *Go on to the hands, wrists and lower arms. Clench the hands, then relax. Let your wrists go floppy. Lift up the lower arms and let them flop back. Then tense and relax the upper arms.*
* *Move on to the shoulders. Hunch them, let them go, wriggle them till they're relaxed. Then relax the neck. Press the head back against the floor or bed, then relax again. Make sure your neck is stretched out straight and your head not twisted to one side.*
* *Then think about your face. Lift your eyebrows, let them go. Squeeze the eyes tight shut, then relax. Frown, then relax. Twitch the nose. Clench and unclench the jaw. Grin, then relax*

the mouth. Let the lips part slightly if they want to and let the jaw sag.

✳ *Concentrate on breathing. Take in a deep breath, let it go, relaxing the chest. Relax the stomach muscles and go on breathing slowly and steadily.*

It can also help you to relax to use visualization techniques. Help your child by telling them they are somewhere lovely and soothing, such as a tropical beach with the sound of the sea in the background, the breeze stirring in the leaves above, the soft feel of the sand and the warmth of the air. Or, if the child seems hot and feverish, you could think of a snowy landscape, a snowman and a Christmas tree, and floating up into the air.

With practice, this technique should rapidly induce a state of relaxation and induce sleep.

The Symmetric Tonic Neck Reflex (STNR)

A specific therapy for ADHD is based on a theory developed by Dr Miriam L. Bender, of Purdue University, in the USA. Her theory is that many children experience behavioural and academic difficulties because of an immature symmetric tonic neck reflex. This reflex is developed in babies at the crawling stage, and ties the neck, arms, and legs together so that when the head is tilted back or forward, tension is increased in the muscles that straighten and flex the elbows, the knees, and the hips.

In normal develoment, the STNR reaches its peak strength at about six to eight months, and has normally diminished by the age of two. If this doesn't happen, however, the reflex hampers rhythmic, co-ordinated movement and makes it very difficult for a child to sit at a desk in the 'correct' position for writing. When a child bends his neck forward and his arms into a writing position, the legs tend to straighten. These children often slouch at the desks with legs straight in front of them. To keep the legs bent, they may hook them round the legs of the chair, another common position seen in fidgety children. They find it hard to sit still for any length of time and are constantly changing position in an attempt to get comfortable.

They often write poorly because every shift of the arm while writing causes a change in the tension in the neck and hips. Copying from the board to the paper is very hard because the constant change in neck position affects the muscles in the arms and legs. Such children often write in a cramped style to minimize movements.

STNR is involved in enabling the baby to crawl. When your baby raises his head, his forearms straighten, pushing his chest from the floor, and his knees and hips bend, pulling him back on to his heels. As your baby learns to crawl, this reflex becomes less important and he gradually gains control over the different parts of his body.

In some infants, however – those who do not learn to crawl – this reflex may not be inhibited. Babies who become 'bottom shufflers', who go straight from sitting to walking, who spend a lot of time in baby walkers, or who crawl for only a short time, may find that the STNR remains active. It's difficult to know whether the problem is a result of babies not crawling or that these babies find crawling difficult because of some problem which is suppressing this reflex. However, Dr Bender's view is that such babies should be encouraged and enabled to crawl, and that children showing ADHD symptoms, who cannot sit still and have problems paying attention, should be taught the proper way of crawling to help suppress the reflex at a later stage.

Dr Miriam Bender's advice for parents of young children is:

✳ *Do place babies on their stomachs from three months old to enable them to push themselves up from the floor*
✳ *Do encourage crawling*
✳ *Allow every opportunity for your baby to crawl*
✳ *Don't put babies in baby walkers*
✳ *Don't overdo the use of playpens*
✳ *Do not encourage early walking*

Dr Bender has developed a programme of exercises for older children designed to help the child's body mature and suppress the STNR. This involves a 26-week programme of exercises of rocking and crawling, more details of which can be found in the book, *Stopping Hyperactivity; A New Solution* by Nancy O'Dell and Patricia A. Cook, who are Directors of the Miriam Bender Diagnostic Center.

5

As they grow

Hyperactive babies

SOME PARENTS of hyperactive children notice that their babies are difficult from the start. Many children who were later diagnosed as ADHD were colicky, fretful, wakeful babies. However, this is not always the case and some parents say ADHD children slept well as babies while other colicky babies settled into tranquil older babies.

Colic is itself a very little understood condition. It is known as 'three months colic' because in many cases the colic and crying stop at around three months – in China it is poetically known as the 'hundred days' crying'. Much research has been done to find out whether colic is in fact caused by wind trapped in the gut, and the current thinking is that it is not. Colic, or crying, may sometimes be caused by stomach pains, but not the regular, all evening or all day crying which some babies are prone to.

Parents who have colicky babies often say that the babies are very tense and irritable. They are easily jolted awake from sleep and never seem to sleep very deeply. Research into sleep in infants has shown that newborn babies have a different sleep pattern to older babies and children. A newborn baby falls first into dreaming sleep and then into deep sleep. At about three months the pattern changes, with the baby dropping into deep sleep and then having patches of dreaming and wakefulness in the night. It may be that in colicky babies some mechanism, perhaps an immaturity in the nervous system or brain wiring, seems to prevent the smooth transition from deep sleep. The baby jerks herself awake after a short patch of dreaming sleep and is then unable to get back to sleep, and cries from tiredness and frustration.

The best way to deal with a colicky baby is to carry her around contained in a sling, or to hold her firmly against your shoulder, supporting her head, so that she cannot flail her limbs or bang her head around. Your baby should be walked or jiggled, and you can also talk to her in a calming voice. Usually she responds to the movement and the sense of security which echoes the way she was coccooned in the womb. Most colicky babies are quiet when in motion, whether being wheeled in the pram, carried in a sling, or driven in a car, so long as they are not hungry. Being rocked rhythmically in your arms, in a rocking cradle or hammock (you can buy special string hammocks, which take a Moses basket, to suspend from a hook in the ceiling) are very soothing, especially when you keep the rhythm to about sixty swings a minute – the same frequency as your heartbeat or your hips when you go for a brisk walk.

Another problem with colicky babies is that they are sometimes difficult to feed, fighting with the breast or bottle. This can happen because when a small baby cries, the first thing we assume is that she is hungry and needs feeding. In fact, the crying baby may not be hungry at all (especially if she has been fed recently). She then takes the breast or teat and starts to suck for comfort, and comes off again because she does not want the food and cries with frustration. If your baby repeatedly goes to the breast or bottle and then pulls away again, it usually means she is not hungry. The best thing to do is end the feed and find something else to do to comfort the baby.

As your baby gets older, you may find that she does not settle down as well as you had hoped. Your baby may still sleep less than other babies and be very demanding and fretful during the day. Unlike other 7–9-month-old babies who are happy to sit with a handful of toys around them, the hyperactive baby will be crawling, rolling and climbing everywhere, will pick something up only to throw it away again a few moments later, and may be constantly whining to be picked up, only to then squirm and protest to be put down again.

If you have this kind of baby, many parents find the best thing to do is to develop a routine and provide lots of stimulation. Such babies often respond well to being taken out to the 'baby bounce' or special activity sessions aimed mainly at toddlers which gives them the opportunity to crawl and run, roll on soft surfaces and use their bodies. They may also enjoy swimming and being taken out of doors.

Toddlers

It is usually when your child becomes a toddler, at the age of between two and three, that a majority of parents realize that their child is different. They may have hoped that their fretful baby would settle down, but then find to their disappointment that she does not get any easier when she is walking, starting to talk, and joining in activities for pre-school children.

The typical toddler with ADHD will not like to be physically restrained in any way. She will climb out of her cot or playpen or stand and scream, rattling the bars. She will struggle with the straps on the pushchair, and try to climb out of the highchair; if she can't, she will scream with frustration. She will find it hard to settle to play, putting one brick on top of another before casting them aside, making one or two marks with a crayon before dropping it, pick up a book and look at it for one or two seconds, and then rush off to something else. She will be hard to feed, picking at food and throwing it around, and not sitting still for long enough to eat a complete meal. Her sleep may be erratic and she may protest about being put to bed or put down for a nap, and sleep only in short bursts.

Such a child is exhausting for the parents and finds it hard to make friends or take part in normal social activities. Other children do not like someone who rushes around, breaking up their games, disrupting their play and who will not take turns or join in.

Many parents hope that their hyperactive child will settle down better once she starts at playgroup or nursery.

Unfortunately, this is not always the case. While she will sometimes benefit from the extra stimulation and activity, and going there may give the exhausted mother a break, she may continue to be difficult to manage. At mother and toddler groups, or playgroups, where the mothers or other carers take it in turns to help on a rota, the hyperactive child may quickly create problems. Her mother may feel unable to leave because her child needs constant supervision or because other parents say they cannot cope.

No matter how hard it seems, it is important to persevere with socializing your child. It is important to give her time one to one where you can help with constructive play, and also time with other children where you can help her learn to wait, listen, and take turns. The following may help in preparing your child for playgroup, nursery or school:

* *Make sure your child looks at you when you speak*
* *Simplify your speech*
* *Slow down your speech*
* *Present instructions in the order in which they are to be carried out*
* *Use visual information, e.g. pictures, gestures, and symbols to support your child's understanding*
* *Describe what the child is going to do, is doing, and has done*
* *Repeat key words and information*

Help your child's language skills by talking to her, singing songs with numbers and rhymes, and by:

✳ *Modelling what your child should have said, e.g. when she says, 'Spoon falled down,' repeat, 'Yes, the spoon fell off'.*
✳ *Expanding simple words, e.g. when she says 'car', say 'Yes, you're driving the car,' or whatever is appropriate for her actions.*

School-age children

When children go to school, ADHD becomes a problem for more than the immediate family; it becomes a problem for the school too. Since ADHD children tend to do better in a situation which is more structured, it is a good idea to visit as many primary schools as you can in your area to see which one is most likely to suit your child. Primary schools which allow children to wander round and select the activity they want to take part in will suit some children, but it is unlikely to bring the best out of a child with ADHD. Look for a nursery where there is a structure and routine to the day.

If your child has been diagnosed with ADHD, it is important to raise the issue with the school before, or as soon as your child starts school. It is a good idea to ask for a meeting with the head and your child's class teacher to explain about her difficulties and what you have been doing at home. It often helps if the school has a strategy for you to back up at home, and vice versa, so that your child is not receiving contradictory messages.

Sometimes ADHD children's problems only become truly apparent when they start school. This is because the difficulties may surface more in a social setting, and when more ordered and concentrated work is expected of them. You may have come to the conclusion that your child is a physical type who likes running around and playing with a ball, but has never been interested in reading quietly or colouring in, and this does not concern you. However, the school will have a different viewpoint. If the teacher comes to you with problems arising from your child's behaviour in school, do listen. Many parents become very defensive and say, 'there was never a problem before she started school'. That may be the case, but it doesn't mean to say that there isn't one now!

ADHD children often find it difficult to settle down in the new environment of school. Problems may arise at particular times, for instance at quiet times when the children are told what to do, or when they have a story at the end of the afternoon and are expected to sit quietly. ADHD children often experience a barrage of criticism at school, so they need to be given opportunities to succeed and to receive praise. Teachers need to be reminded that a combination of positive rewards and praise for good behaviour coupled with ignoring and then punishing disruptive behaviour is best.

It may be that school will need extra help to cope with your child. They may need a special helper in the classroom to supervize and give her extra input. Many ADHD children will need instructions to be repeated and will need to work in short bursts with time for physical activity in between. If your child is quite severely affected, if may help if you work with the school to get extra help in the classroom.

If your child has not been diagnosed as having ADHD, the school may suggest than an educational psychologist is called in to help make a diagnosis. An assessment may be made involving a psychologist, a doctor and other health professionals. If it is decided that your child has special needs extra help may be provided, perhaps in the form of an extra staff member in the classroom or additional one to one sessions.

Inevitably in a school where there are many children in a class, it is going to be difficult for teachers to make adjustments in the way they teach to make life easier for your child. However, if they can make certain changes, it will help make her easier to manage to everybody's benefit. The more organized the classroom is, the easier it will be for her to know what to do. It's important that the teacher lays stress on what she *should* be doing rather than what she shouldn't.

Writing down instructions as well as giving them verbally can help. Instructions should be given one at a time, clearly and simply. Making eye contact with your child helps. She can be asked to repeat instructions to show that she has understood. Breaking an assignment down into several small, manageable tasks can also help and your child may need help to know how much time to spend on each part. Positive feedback will help boost her self-esteem and make her more willing to learn.

Teachers can gain your child's attention by using her name, touching her shoulder or arm, or using a prearranged non-verbal signal. Avoiding constant tellings off is important, and giving praise where merited will result in improved behaviour.

It is also important that if your child does fall behind with work, that break-times and lunch hours are not used to make her catch up. Your child needs this time to run around and be physically active. If she needs a break, she could be sent on an errand or given some physical activity to do.

If your child is very disruptive in the classroom, this can obviously affect the other children's learning and clearly cannot be ignored. Teachers need to work out a consistent strategy for dealing with inappropriate behaviour. The best one is first to ignore it, then if the negative behaviour continues, interrupt it, state what behaviour is appropriate and then, if the behaviour still continues, use 'time out'.

Some ADHD children will need to take medication at school, normally Ritalin. Since the medication used for ADHD only lasts 3–4 hours, a child will need to take a midday dose. Most young children will not be able to take responsibility for this themselves, and many ADHD children are chaotic and find it difficult to remember whether they have taken their medication or not, even when they are older. Schools are not legally obliged to give children medication; some are willing, others are not. It is important to speak to the head teacher and class teacher at your child's school to explain the problem and the importance of your child taking her medication. Most will be willing to help in some way, even if it involves checking your child has taken her medication rather than giving it directly.

Teenagers

About 70 per cent of children diagnosed with ADHD still continue to have it in adolescence, and about 10 per cent will carry it on into adulthood. While many ADHD children become quieter and less hyperactive as they become older, the attention deficit problems often remain. This inevitably affects your child's ability to learn in school, her relationship with her family and her sense of self-esteem.

Teenagers are inevitably very conscious of any differences they may have to other children. They are frequently anxious about what other people think of them and are particuarly vulnerable to criticism. If your child receives constant criticism she will switch off. She may feel that she is not doing well at school, so is not going to try. Without help and skilled intervention, a vicious cycle can begin.

It is more important than ever to give your child praise wherever possible and to try to break into the cycle of low self-esteem and poor behaviour. Try to get your child involved in physical activities such as sports or swimming. Reward and praise good behaviour, try to ignore bad behaviour unless it escalates out of control. Try to keep track of your child's social life; if she seems to form unsuitable friendships, try to provide attractive alternatives rather than just criticizing her friends or forbidding her to see them. You may need to liaise with teachers and school to ensure that your child gets the most out of her educational opportunities.

FAILURE AT SCHOOL

Many ADHD children fail at school. This may have started in primary school and, by the time the children are preparing for important exams, they may be far behind their contemporaries and know that they are not going to succeed. Without educational qualifications, their chances of getting well-paid employment fall dramatically. As unskilled manual work is less and less available, these young people can frequently feel worthless.

Families may find it harder and harder to cope with their teenager. A young child can be more easily controlled than an angry teenager. Once parents find their children are bigger and stronger than they are, they may feel threatened and unable to cope. This can apply particularly to a single mother, or a mother whose partner is often absent at work, in charge of a teenage boy, especially if he is aggressive as well as impulsive.

Teenagers with ADHD tend to be viewed even more negatively than younger children. Sometimes family relationships break down completely, and in the UK it has been estimated that 40 per cent of adolescents in care have ADHD or a behavioural disorder, or both. Many ADHD children do not get support at school and their behaviour may result in suspensions, exclusions or even expulsion, with devastating results for their future.

It is important to make sure the school are aware of your child's problems and seek their support in finding solutions. They are much more likely to be helpful and co-operative if you explain the situation in advance and show that you are willing to assist in whatever way may be necessary. Many schools now have contracts between the child, the parent and the school to make sure that homework is done, rules are obeyed, and that a child is receiving the same message from both parents and schools. It is unwise ever to get into a battle in which you blame the school for your child's failure. It is far more constructive to work together, and much more likely to help resolve any difficulties.

TROUBLE WITH THE POLICE

Research has shown that ADHD adolescents are far more likely than others to get into trouble with the police. This may be because of their greater impulsiveness, or because they find schooling so unrewarding that they start to stay away from school and get involved in crime. A teenager's peer group is extremely important and children not attending school are likely to make contact with others who are involved in undesirable activities.

One study has shown that hyperactivity, impulsiveness and attention deficit in eight-year-olds predicted delinquency in adolescence. Some researchers believe that ADHD is linked to personality disorders in adults, and there is some thinking that personality disorders could be undiagnosed ADHD in adults. However, this does not mean that every ADHD child is likely to grow up to lead a life of crime. It simply points out that there is this potential, if the child's needs are not recognized, if her family cannot cope and rejects her, if she is not helped in school and finds herself without educational qualifications or any kind of support.

Teenagers with ADHD, even more than younger children, need to have their self-esteem boosted. One way in which they can excel is in sport, so any extra help you can give in paying for sporting activities and training is likely to reap dividends. ADHD children who are physically active may then be more able to concentrate when this is expected of them. Team sports are also good for helping children to socialize, work together, and make friendships, which is often more difficult for the ADHD child in school.

Sometimes ADHD children may benefit from going to a specialist school where their particular needs can be met. Unfortunately for many parents, this often means special units for children who have a wide variety of education, behavioural and emotional problems, which does not always help your child. Many parents, therefore, prefer to pay for private schooling where their child will be in a small class, where there are more teachers and helpers, and often far better sports facilities.

In conclusion

Parents should not think that if their child is diagnosed with ADHD the future is bleak; far from it. The majority of hyperactive children will grow out of their problems and if their energy can be harnessed in a positive direction they can be high achievers. Many ADHD children will do well at school with extra help, and there is treatment available which can help where there are real problems. Others will never do well at school, but can still be helped to form good relationships with their peers, their teachers, and their family.

Many of the therapies listed in this book can give enormous benefits to children with ADHD. With firmness, love, support, and help many will thrive. Most of all these children should not be dismissed as naughty, disobedient and lazy, but be given understanding and the practical help they need to enable them to fulfil their individual potential and lead a full and happy life.

Appendix

ADHD Criteria

Table 1:
Attention Deficit Hyperactivity Disorder (ADHD): A. either (1) or (2)

(1) SIX (OR MORE) OF THE FOLLOWING SYMPTOMS OF INATTENTION HAVE PERSISTED FOR AT LEAST SIX MONTHS TO A DEGREE THAT IS MALADAPTIVE AND INCONSISTENT WITH DEVELOPMENTAL LEVEL.

INATTENTION

A	Often fails to give close attention to details or makes careless mistakes in schoolwork, work or other activities.
B	Often has difficulty sustaining attention in tasks or play activities.
C	Often does not seem to listen when spoken to directly.
D	Often does not seem to follow through on instructions and fails to finish schoolwork, chores or duties in the workplace (not due to oppositional behaviour or failure to understand instructions).
E	Often has difficulty organising tasks and activities.
F	Often avoids, dislikes or is reluctant to engage in tasks that require sustained mental effort (such as schoolwork or homework)
G	Often loses things necessary to tasks or activities (e.g. toys, school assignments, pencils, books, or tools).

| **H** | Is often distracted by extraneous stimuli. |

| **I** | Is often forgetful in daily activities. |

(2) SIX, OR MORE, OF THE FOLLOWING SYMPTOMS OF HYPERACTIVITY–IMPULSIVITY HAVE PERSISTED FOR AT LEAST SIX MONTHS TO A DEGREE THAT IS MALADAPTIVE AND INCONSISTENT WITH DEVELOPMENT LEVEL.

HYPERACTIVITY

| **A** | Often fidgets with hands or feet, or squirms in seat. |

| **B** | Often leaves seat in classroom or other situation where it is inappropriate (in adolescents or adults, this may be limited to subjective feelings of restlessness).[1] |

| **C** | Often has difficulty playing or engaging in leisure activities quietly.[2] |

| **D** | Is often 'on the go' or often acts as if 'driven by a motor'.[3] |

| **E** | Often talks excessively.[4] |

IMPULSIVITY

| **F** | Often blurts out answers before questions have been completed. |

| **G** | Often has difficulty awaiting turn. |

| **H** | Often interrupts or intrudes on others (e.g. butts into conversations or games). |

[1] Some hyperactive–impulsive or inattentive symptoms that caused impairment were present before the age of 7 years.

[2] Some impairment from the symptoms is present in two or more settings (e.g. at school (or work) and at home).

3   There must be clear evidence of clinically significant impairment in social, academic or occupational functioning.

4   The symptoms do not occur exclusively during the course of a Pervasive Developmental Disorder, Schizophrenia, or other Psychotic Disorder, and are not better accounted for by another mental disorder (e.g. Mood Disorder, Anxiety Disorder, Dissociative Disorder, or a Personality Disorder.

Table 2:
Oppositional Defiant Disorder (ODD)

1	Often loses temper.
2	Often argues with adults.
3	Often actively defies or refuses adult's requests or rules, e.g. refuses to do chores at home.
4	Often deliberately does things that annoy other people, e.g. grabs other children's hats.
5	Often blames others for his mistakes.
6	Is often touchy or easily annoyed by others.
7	Is often angry and resentful.
8	Is often spiteful and vindictive.
9	Often swears or uses obscene language.
(i)	At least 5 of the above 9 behaviours should be present more than is usual for peer group.
(ii)	ODD usually begins by age 18.

ODD may evolve into a conduct disorder.

Table 3:
Conduct Disorder

1   Has stolen without confrontation of a victim on more than one occasion (including forgery).

2   Has run away from home overnight at least twice while living in parental or surrogate home (or once without returning).

3   Often lies (other than to avoid physical or sexual abuse).

4   Has deliberately engaged in fire setting.

5   Is often truant from school (for older person, absent from work)

6   Has broken into someone's else's house, building or car.

7   Has deliberately destroyed other's property
(other than by fire setting)

8   Has been physically cruel to animals.

9   Has forced someone into sexual activity with him or her.

10 Has used a weapon in more than one fight.

11 Often initiates physical fights.

12 Has stolen with confrontation of a victim (e.g. mugging, purse snatching, extortion, armed robbery).

13 Has been physically cruel to people.

At least 3 of the above should be present for a minimum of 6 months.

Further reading

ON HYPERACTIVITY:

Is My Child Hyperactive?, Jo
Douglas, Penguin, 1991

*Understanding Your Hyperactive
Child: The Essential Guide For
Parents*, Professor Eric Taylor,
Vermilion, 1995

*Stopping Hyperactvity: A New
Solution*, Nancy O'Dell and
Patricia A. Cook, Avery
Publishing, New York, 1997

ON ALTERNATIVE REMEDIES:

*Aromatherapy For Babies and
Children*, Shirley Price and Penny
Price Parr, Thorsons, 1996

Acupuncture for Everyone, Dr
Ruth Lever, Penguin, 1987

*Miranda Castro's Homeopathic
Guide: Mother and Baby*, Pan, 1992

*The Encyclopedia of Flower
Remedies*, Clare Harvey and
Amanda Cochrane, Thorsons,
1995

The New Holistic Herbal, David
Hoffmann, Element Books, 1990

*Back to Balance: A Self-Help
Encyclopedia of Eastern Holistic
Remedies*, (USA and Japan)
Kodansha International, 1996;
(UK) Newleaf, 1996

The Elimination Diet Cookbook,
Jill Carter and Alison Edwards,
Element Books, 1997

The Rotation Diet Cookbook, Jill
Carter and Alison Edwards,
Element Books, 1997

Nutritional Medicine, Dr Stephen
Davies and Dr Alan Stewart, Pan,
1987

Useful addresses

UNITED KINGDOM

Action Against Allergy
43 The Downs
London SW20 SHG

*Association for Children with
Learning Difficulties*
Quirral House, Pitch Place
Thursley
Godalming
Surrey GU8 6QW

Association of Reflexologists
27 Old Gloucester Street
London W1N 3XX
Tel: 0990 673320

British Association for Counselling
1 Regent Place
Rugby
Warwickshire CV21 2PJ
Tel: 01788 578328

British Epilepsy Association
Anstey House
40 Hanover Square
Leeds
Yorks LS3 1BE

British Homeopathic Association
27a Devonshire Street
London W1N 1RJ

*British Institute for Brain
Injured Children*
Knowle Hall
Knowle
Bridgwater
Somerset TA7 8PJ
Tel: 01278 684060

*British Society of Medical and
Dental Hypnosis*
42 Links Road
Ashtead
Surrey KT21 2HJ
Tel: 01372 273522

*CALIP (Campaign Against Lead
in Petrol)*
63 Dora Road
London SW19 7HH

*Camphill Rudolf Steiner School
(Central Office)*
Murtle House
Bieldside
Aberdeen

*CLEAR (The Campaign for Lead
Free Air)*
2 Northdown Street
London NI 9BC

Council for Acupuncture
179 Gloucester Place
London NW1 6DX
0171 724 5756

*Council for Complementary and
Alternative Medicine*
179 Gloucester Place
London NW1 6DX
Tel: 0171 7249103

Food Allergy Association
c/o The Chairman
Mrs Ellen Rothera
27 Ferringham Lane
Ferring
West Sussex BN12 5NB

*Hyperactive Children's Support
Group (HACSG)*
71 Whyke Lane
Chichester
West Sussex PO19 2LD
Tel: 01903 725182

National Children's Bureau
8 Wakley Street
Islington
London ECIV 7QE
Tel: 0171 843 6000

*National Society for Prevention of
Cruelty to Children*
67 Saffron Hill
London ECIN SRS
Tel: 0171 242 1626

*Register of Traditional
Chinese Medicine*
19 Trinity Road
London N2 8JJ
Tel: 0181 883 8431

CANADA

*Canadian Holistic Medical
Association*
700 Bay Street
PO Box 101, Suite 604
Toronto
Ontario M5G 1Z6
Tel: 416 599 0447

*Canadian Institute of Child
Health*
17 York Street
Suite 202
Ottawa
Ontario KIN 5S7

Canadian Paediatric Society
Centre hospitalier universitaire de

Sherbrooke
Sherbrooke
Quebec J1H 5N4

*Human Nutrition Research
Council of Ontario*
PO Box 38
Stittsville
Ontario KOA 3GO

*Society for Emotionally Disturbed
Children*
1622 Sherbrooke Street West
3rd Floor
Montreal
Quebec H3H 1C9

AUSTRALIA

*Active Hyperkinetic Children's
Association*
PO Box 17
East Doneaster Victoria 3109

*Australian Natural Therapists
Association*
PO Box 308
Melrose Park
South Australia 5039
Tel: 8297 9533

*Hyperactivity Association
of NSW*
24/29 Bertram Street
Chatswood NSW 2067

*Hyperactivity Association of South
Australia Inc*
18 King William Road
North Adelaide SA 5006

Hyperactive Help (WA)
88 Manning Street
Scarborough WA 6019

*Launceston Hyperactivity
Association*
Mrs P. Motton
C/- PO
Meander
Tasmania 7304

Mackay Hyperactivity Association
PO Box 204
Mackay
Queensland 4740

*Queensland Hyperactivity
Association*
PO Box 107 Veronga
Queensland 4104

NEW ZEALAND

*Auckland Hyperactivity
Association Inc*
PO Box 36-099
Northcote
Auckland NZ

*Waikato Hyperkinetic Children's
Support Group*
C/- 10 McFarlane Street
Hamilton NZ

*Wellington Hyperactivity and
Allergy Association Inc*
93 Waipapa Road
Hataitai
Wellington NZ

USA

*American Association of
Naturopathic Physicians*
2800 East Madison Street
Suite 200
Seattle WA 98102

Tel: 206 323 7610
*American Holistic Medicine
Association*
4101 Lake Boone Trail Suite 201
Raleigh NC 27607
Tel: 919 787 5146

*Children and Adults with
Attention Deficit Disorder
(CHADD)*
8181 Professional Place,
Suite 201
Landover, MD 20785
Tel: (800) 233 4050
301 306 7070
email: national@chadd.org
website: http://www.chadd.org

*Feingold Association
of the US*
PO Box 6550
Alexandra VA 22306

*The National Attention Deficit
Disorder Association (National
ADDA)*
PO Box 1303
Northbrook, IL 60065-1304
Tel: 440 350 9595
email: DearADDA@aol.com
website: http://www.add.org

Index

THE ELEMENT FAMILY ENCYCLOPEDIA OF HEALTH

Dr R. Sharma

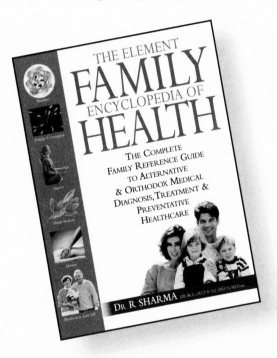

Anyone with an interest in healthcare should have this unique reference guide which covers both orthodox and complementary treatments in equal depth. This thorough and authoritative encyclopedia provides expert advice for most common medical conditions and covers all ages from conception through childhood to maturity. Contains over 200 illustrations including diagrams, charts and photographs.

255 x 189 mm, 2-colour printing with black & white illustrations, 640 pages ISBN: 1 86204 301 9
£24.99 hardback US **$34.95** / CAN **$43.99**

TO ORDER

UK: Please call the credit card order line on **0870 2413065** or fax your order to **01747 851394**.
For postal orders please send a cheque or postal order made payable to Element Books, together with your name and address
and the completed order form; (photocopies accepted) to: **Element Direct, Longmead, Shaftesbury, Dorset, SP7 8PL.**
Postage & packing free. *Please quote code YR1 on all orders*

US: Please call **1 800 788 6262** or Fax: **201 896 8569**. Please have your Visa, Mastercard or American Express reasy.
You will be charged at the list price plus a shipping and handling fee and any applicable sales tax.

CANADA: Orders to: **Penguin Books Canada Ltd, c/o Canbook Distribution Center,**
1220 Nicholson Road, Newmarket, Ontario L3V 7V1.
Toll-Free Customer Service
Canada-wide Tel: **1 800 399 6858** Canada-wide Fax: **1 800 363 2665** Toronto line: **905 713 3852**

TITLE	ISBN	PRICE	QUANITY	TOTAL PRICE
			TOTAL	

All UK and European trade enquiries should be directed to
Penguin Books Ltd, Bath Road, Harmondsworth, West Drayton, Middlesex. UB7 0DA. Tel: 0181 8994036
For information on Element Books and how to order them outside the UK please contact your appropriate distributor.
(Prices correct at time of going to press, all books subject to availability)

AUSTRALIA
Penguin Books Australia Ltd
487 Maroondah Highway, PO Box 257, Ringwood, Victoria
3134, Australia
Tel: (3) 9871 2400, Fax: (3) 9870 9618

NEW ZEALAND
Penguin Books New Zealand Ltd
182-190 Wairau Road, Private Bag 102902,
North Shore Mail Centre, Auckland 10, New Zealand
Tel: (9) 415 4700, Fax: (9) 415 4704
or (customer services) 444 1470

SOUTH AFRICA
Penguin Books South Africa (Pty) Ltd
Private Bag X1, Park View, 2122 Johannesburg,
South Africa
Tel: (11) 482 1520, Fax: (11) 482 6669

CENTRAL & SOUTH AMERICA
Book Business International
Rue Dr Estdras Pacheco Ferreira 200, 04507 0 060
Vila Nova Conceicao, Sao Paulo SP, Brazil
Tel: (11) 884 2198, Fax: (11) 884 2198

PHILIPPINES
Penguin Putnam Inc.
375 Hudson Street, New York, NY 10014, USA
Tel: (212) 366 2000, Fax: (212) 366 2940

INDIA, SRI LANKA & BANGLADESH
Penguin Books India Pvt Ltd
11 Community Centre, Panchsheel Park,
New Delhi 110017, India
Tel: (11) 649 4401/649 4405, Fax: (11) 649 4402

PAKISTAN
Book Com
Main Chambers, 3 Temple Road, GPO Box 518,
Lahore, Pakistan
Tel: (42) 636 7275, Fax: (42) 636 1370

JAPAN
Penguin Books Japan Ltd
Kaneko Building, 2-3-25 Koraku, Bunkyo-ku,
Tokyo 112, Japan
Tel: (3) 3815 6840, Fax: (3) 3815 6841

SOUTH EAST ASIA/FAR EAST
Penguin Books Ltd
2nd Floor, Cornwall House, Taikoo Place,
979 King's Road, Quarry Bay, Hong Kong
Tel: (852) 2 856 6448, Fax: (852) 2 579 0119

SINGAPORE
STP Distributors Pte Ltd
Books Division, Pasir Panjang Districentre, Block 1,
No. 03-01, Pasir Panjang Road, Singapore 0511
Tel: 276 7626, Fax: 276 7119

ELEMENT